The Play of the Royal Astrologers

A Play by

Willis Hall

Samuel French - London
New York - Toronto - Hollywood

CHARACTERS

The Chancellor
The Emperor
The Emperor's Daughter
Father Mole-Cricket
Master Mole-Cricket
Mother Mole-Cricket
First Villager*
Second Villager*
Wizard*
Palace Messenger*
Leader of the Thieves*
First Thief*
Second Thief*
Third Thief*
First Sailor—Henry*
Second Sailor—Fred*
First Mate*
Captain Beanfeast*
First Palace Guard*
Second Palace Guard*

(All the characters marked with an asterisk appear in one scene only, they can, therefore, be doubled, if necessary.)

ACT I

SCENE 1

Before the CURTAIN *rises the Chancellor, a tall harassed man with a long beard, dressed in flowing robes, bustles across the stage and addresses the audience across the "footlights"*

Chancellor Ah, there you are! I've been looking for you everywhere! Something dreadful has happened. Too horrible for words. Goodness only knows what will happen to me when they find out. I shall lose my head, that's a certainty. Off—clean as a whistle. And there's nothing I can do about it. Nothing. You see, the truth is, promise not to laugh, the truth is—I've lost the Emperor. One minute he was standing right next to me, the next moment he was gone. He'll say it was my fault of course. He always does. There we were, all ready to begin the play and now this has to happen. I don't suppose, by any chance, that any of you have seen the Emperor? . . . No? No, I didn't think so. I don't know what we're going to do now. I just don't know . . . You wouldn't care to come back tomorrow? Or next week say? . . . No? No, I didn't think that you would. There is only one thing for it—we must carry on without him, that's all. We'll begin now.

This is a play about the Emperor, Indera Maya, and about the lands of Indera Maya, and about the peoples of Indera Maya. The Emperor rules over a beautiful and prosperous country, set amongst the tallest tips of the distant mountains, which wear clouds for bonnets and change their bonnets twice a day. At the foot of the mountains is a forest, and beyond the forest is a desert, and beyond the desert is the edge of the world . . .

As for the people of Indera Maya—myself included (I, by the way, am the Emperor's Chancellor and by far the most important person you will see this evening), the people of Indera Maya are a happy people. Every year, in every village, they plough their fields, plant their grain, water their crops and gather their harvest; for the subjects of Indera Maya are the hardest working people in the whole world . . .

But wait—you shall see for yourselves. (*He calls off, into the wings*) You there! Peasant! Take up this curtain! We are about to begin! . . . Thank you.

The back garden of the Mole-Cricket family

The rear of the set is taken up with the exterior of the Mole-Cricket house—a rickety construction of bamboo and thatched palm. A small veranda and door lead into the house

Two figures, both dressed in peasant costume, lie in the shade of a small tree. They are asleep and snoring heavily. The larger of the two is Father Mole-Cricket and the smaller his son, Master Mole-Cricket

The Chancellor moves into the set and continues

As I was saying, the subjects of Indera Maya are the hardest working people in the whole world. The two . . . er . . . persons you see here are the exception. This one is Father Mole-Cricket.

The Chancellor nudges the sleeping form of Father Mole-Cricket with his foot. Father Mole-Cricket stirs but does not waken

And this one is his son, Master Mole-Cricket. As a matter of fact, these two aren't at all hard-working. As a matter of fact, they have been described as lazy. As a matter of fact, it has been said that these two are the laziest pair in all the world. But I shall wake them and you may judge for yourselves . . . (*He raises his foot as if to bestow a kick upon the seat of Father Mole-Cricket, but his eye is caught by something in the wings and his foot is lowered*) Excuse me a moment . . . I thought I saw . . . (*He peers again off stage*) It is! His Majesty! His Most Imperial Majesty! He's arrived! What did I tell you! Majesty! Wait for me! I'm here, Majesty! I'm coming! . . . I'm coming! (*He moves off* L. *He pauses before making his exit and again addresses the audience*) Pardon me, but I must speak to his Majesty. Don't worry. I'll be back again later.

The Chancellor bustles off

There is a pause as the two Mole-Crickets continue to snore and then, slowly and carefully, Father Mole-Cricket lifts himself up and yawns loud and long. Master Mole-Cricket does the same

Father Mole-Cricket What are you doing, my son?
Master Mole-Cricket Nothing, Father. I just yawned.
Father Mole-Cricket Oh.
Master Mole-Cricket A thought crossed my mind and so I yawned.
Father Mole-Cricket Oh.
Master Mole-Cricket I had an idea.
Father Mole-Cricket And it made you yawn?
Master Mole-Cricket Yes, Father.
Father Mole-Cricket What kind of idea was it?
Master Mole-Cricket Just a . . . Well . . . I'm too tired to remember, Father.
Father Mole-Cricket Then we might as well go back to sleep.
Master Mole-Cricket Yes . . . Wait a minute! It's coming back to me! I know what it was! I thought I might go into the house and get something to eat.
Father Mole-Cricket Oh . . . I don't think there is anything to eat, my boy.
Master Mole-Cricket Isn't there? . . . Oh, well, it doesn't really matter.
Father Mole-Cricket No.
Master Mole-Cricket I shall just lie here in the warm afternoon sun until it is cool, and then I shall go to bed. That's an even better idea, isn't it, Father?

Father Mole-Cricket, having already nodded off to sleep, does not reply

Father. (*He shakes Father Mole-Cricket roughly*) Father!
Father Mole-Cricket (*opening one eye*) Mmmmmm?
Master Mole-Cricket You haven't answered me.
Father Mole-Cricket I don't think there is anything to eat.
Master Mole-Cricket You said that before.
Father Mole-Cricket Did I? . . . Then I have said enough to be going on with. I can't keep saying things all the time.. It makes me tired . . .
Master Mole-Cricket It . . . It makes me feel tired, too, Father . . .
Father Mole-Cricket Then the best thing to do . . . is . . . go to . . . sleep . . .

They lie down and immediately begin to snore

The door to the house opens and Mother Mole-Cricket comes out. She carries an empty cooking pot. She moves down the veranda and across to the two sleeping figures

Mother Mole-Cricket (*digging Father Mole-Cricket in the ribs with the cooking pot*) Idler! Loafer! Good-for-nothing! Wastrel! Are you going to lie there and sleep all day?
Father Mole-Cricket It's a very good suggestion, my love. But I don't quite see how we can. (*He rises reluctantly*) Not if you keep interrupting us, we can't.
Mother Mole-Cricket What about the work? What about the house? What about the farm? What about the roof you were going to mend on the chicken run?
Father Mole-Cricket (*yawning*) Tomorrow, my love. I shall see to all those things tomorrow.
Mother Mole-Cricket And what about the yard? And the broken fence? To say nothing about the water to be carried from the well and the wood to be chopped.
Father Mole-Cricket The day after tomorrow.
Mother Mole-Cricket And the floor to be swept and the chimneys to be cleaned and the fowls to be fed and the——
Father Mole-Cricket The day after the day after to——
Mother Mole-Cricket Idler! Idiot! And what do you think you're going to do today?
Father Mole-Cricket Perfectly simple, my dear. Today I'm going to sit here, in the warmth of the sun, and plan all those things I intend to do tomorrow and the day after tomorrow and the day after the day after tomorrow.
Mother Mole-Cricket And who is to plant the rice? Tell me that!
Father Mole-Cricket Rice! Ah, rice! Strange you should mention rice, my love. Now there you have a commodity. Have you ever considered, beloved, the amount of rice consumed per square stomach in this village alone?
Mother Mole-Cricket Oh . . . !
Father Mole-Cricket I assure you, my dear, the figures would astonish you. As a matter of fact, believe it or not, I was only in the process of

constructing a little philosophy on that very subject not two moments ago. Give a man a bag of rice and what does he do? Eat it? No. He plants it, and tends it, and waters it—which is work. Fact number one. To work makes him hungry. Fact number two. So what does he do? Why, he harvests the rice he planted and eats it! Fact number three. And where has it all got him, eh? Nowhere. He might just as well have eaten the bag of rice in the first place. A man either eats to work or works to eat. I worked all that out on my own. You should be pleased, dear heart, to have a husband who has struggled the hard path towards spiritual contentment.

Mother Mole-Cricket Pleased, should I? Then you should be pleased to have a wife with nothing to cook for the dinner tomorrow. (*She raises the cooking pot menacingly*) And nothing to cook for the dinner the day after tomorrow, and nothing for the day after the day after . . .

Father Mole-Cricket All right, my love! I'll think of something. Never you fear. Just you leave it to me.

Mother Mole-Cricket If I left it to you we should never eat at all, we should never do anything but sleep. And as for that son of yours . . .

Father Mole-Cricket And yours, dear one, and yours.

Mother Mole-Cricket Don't argue. As for that son of yours . . . Look at him! Just look at him!

They both survey the sleeping figure

Father Mole-Cricket (*with pride*) A fine lad! A fine lad indeed!

Mother Mole-Cricket Why, he's only awake twice a day: once to get out of bed and again to get into it. I can't imagine why he ever takes the trouble to get out of bed at all.

Father Mole-Cricket Now that you come to mention it, my dear—neither can I. I'll ask him, if you like, the next time we're both awake together.

Mother Mole-Cricket You'll do nothing of the sort. You'll go out and find some work. Both of you. Now.

Master Mole-Cricket (*sitting bolt upright with shock*) Work? Work! Did someone say something about work? I . . . I was just dozing.

Mother Mole-Cricket I did. I said you must go and earn some money. Now!

Master Mole-Cricket Work! *Earn* money! (*He scrambles to his feet*) But, Mother . . .

Mother Mole-Cricket You heard me. I shall light the fire and put on the pot, by which time I shall expect you both back here with something for the evening meal . . .

Master Mole-Cricket Mother!

Father Mole-Cricket Now, my love! Patience! We mustn't run into this business foolhardily, you know. Dear me, no. Now . . . Let me think . . . I know! We'll borrow something! How's that?

Master Mole-Cricket Hopeless. Everyone is in the fields at work.

Mother Mole-Cricket Where you idle pair should be.

Father Mole-Cricket Hush, my love, and let me think . . . Ah, yes! I have it! Yes, yes! Capital! I can't imagine why I never thought of it before!

Mother Mole-Cricket You were probably asleep at the time.

Father Mole-Cricket Listen, my boy, I'll explain my plan. You must go down to the rice fields where our good neighbours are at work — God bless their simple souls. And then you must hide in the long grass by the edge of the stream . . .

Master Mole-Cricket And then?

Father Mole-Cricket And then, bide your time carefully, and when no-one is looking, take two of their buffaloes and hide them somewhere out of sight. Hide them in the bushes just past the end of the village.

Master Mole-Cricket I don't see where all this is getting us.

Father Mole-Cricket Will you listen to me! I'm telling you, aren't I? When the villagers notice that the animals are missing, tell them that your father knows a little about — astrology.

Master Mole-Cricket Astra-what-a-gy?

Father Mole-Cricket Ology. The study of the stars, my son.

Master Mole-Cricket Astrology.

Father Mole-Cricket Tell them, in fact, that your father is an astrologer!

Master Mole-Cricket As-what-a-ger?

Father Mole-Cricket Astrologer. And that by studying the stars I may be able to help them.

Master Mole-Cricket I don't quite see, Father, what the stars have got to do with buffaloes.

Father Mole-Cricket Never mind, my boy. You leave all that to your clever old father. Just you tell the villagers all that I have said. Bring them here. And leave the rest to me.

Master Mole-Cricket Wait a minute! I think I'm beginning to understand! You'll tell the villagers where to find their buffaloes, they'll be pleased and . . .

Father Mole-Cricket Just so.

Mother Mole-Cricket Astrology indeed! What nonsense!

Master Mole-Cricket If you ask me, Father, I think it's the best idea you ever had.

Father Mole-Cricket Thank you, my boy.

Master Mole-Cricket Although, I would like to make one small suggestion . . .

Father Mole-Cricket Yes?

Master Mole-Cricket How would it be, Father, if you went down to the fields and took the buffaloes? You see, it's a very dusty road, and it is hot, and I'm not feeling very well today. If you were to go I could lie down here for a little while. By the time you got back I'm sure I should be . . .

Father Mole-Cricket Sometimes, my boy, I feel ashamed of you. I do really. Here am I, your poor, tired, old father, and you suggest that I go walking in the hot fields and hide buffaloes and watch everyone working and . . . and . . . Oh dear! I'm beginning to feel quite faint!

Master Mole-Cricket Very well, Father. I was just going. But, I still can't see why——

Father Mole-Cricket That's better, my boy. Don't forget what I've told you!

Master Mole-Cricket Very well, Father . . . (*He moves away but has only walked a few paces before he is asleep on his feet*)

Mother Mole-Cricket (*crossing to Master Mole-Cricket and shaking him vigorously*) And don't fall asleep on the way!

Master Mole-Cricket (*stifling a yawn*) Very well, Mother. . . .

Master Mole-Cricket trudges off

Father Mole-Cricket You see, my love, all our worries are at an end. And all because your wise and diligent husband has been using his brains. (*He prepares to seat himself on the grass*) And now that's done I can just . . . (*He yawns*) . . . I can just . . .

Mother Mole-Cricket (*crossing to his side*) You can just what?

Father Mole-Cricket Well, my dear, I was just going to . . . that is to say . . . at least I . . . and then after that I was . . . at least I thought I might . . .

Mother Mole-Cricket I have a better idea. Come along, you can peel the onions for supper.

Father Mole-Cricket Peel the onions? But, my love, I was . . .

Mother Mole-Cricket (*taking a firm grasp of his ear*) I said, come along!

Father Mole-Cricket Very well, my love. Very well. I'm coming.

Mother Mole-Cricket (*leading him unceremoniously onto the veranda*) And when you've finished them I'm sure I'll be able to find you something else to keep you busy.

They exit, Father Mole-Cricket protesting loudly, through the door and into the house

There is a pause before the Chancellor enters L

At the same time the Emperor, a short and fussy monarch, enters R

They are both peering into the respective wings from which they made their entrances and slowly each walks backward towards the centre of the stage. When they are but a few inches apart, neither being aware of the other, the Emperor draws himself erect and calls out in a loud voice

Emperor Chancellor!

Chancellor (*swinging round in surprise*) Majesty!

Emperor (*equally surprised*) There you are, Chancellor!

Chancellor Here I am, indeed, Majesty! (*He bows low*)

Emperor Well, it won't do, Chancellor! It just won't do! Here am I, searching high and low, up and down, round and about, all over the kingdom for you—and here are you playing hide and seek behind my back in front of my nose.

Chancellor A thousand apologies, Majesty. A thousand, thousand apologies. Indeed, I too, have been looking for you.

Emperor You'd no business to do anything of the kind, Chancellor. You should have stood quite still where you were—and not started scurrying about looking for where I were—was—were——

The Chancellor, in his agitation, is bowing low many times

And for goodness sake, man, stop bobbing up and down like a yo-yo. You make me feel quite ill.

Chancellor A thousand, thousand, thousand apologies, Majesty.

Emperor And stop calling out numbers, Chancellor! You know very well I hate numbers. Really, Chancellor! You must learn to control your emotions. You do lose your head so easily.

Chancellor Do I, Majesty?

Emperor You do indeed. One of these days I can see that you are going to lose it altogether. (*He draws a significant finger across his throat*)

Chancellor I'm sure I do my utmost to please your Majesty, your Majesty.

Emperor Then it isn't utmost enough. I have more than enough to do, I would remind you, without having to spend my afternoons running all over the countryside looking for my Chancellor.

Chancellor But it was so late, Majesty. And I knew that you would be annoyed if we ventured to begin without you, and before I could find you everyone had arrived and——

Emperor Will you speak plainly! Will you speak audibly! Will you make yourself understood! Start? Start? Start what? What are you whispering into your whiskers now, man! Start what?

Chancellor The play, Majesty.

Emperor Play? Play? I've no wish to play, Chancellor! Now look here! Listen to me! I spend all my time scouring the district for you, I finally run you to earth in this broken-down back-yard, I'm hot, I'm tired, my robes are too heavy, my feet are burning, my head aches, I'm out of breath and, worst of all, I've lost my temper—and you calmly stand there and tell me it's all been some silly sort of game.

Chancellor Indeed no, Majesty, you see——

Emperor Indeed yes, Chancellor. And I don't see, no. (*He draws the Chancellor towards him and they move downstage*) Now, listen carefully, Chancellor. Pay attention. For while you've been hopping around in your back-yards, hiding and seeking whatever it is you've been seeking and hiding—a crime has been commited.

Chancellor Crime, Majesty?

Emperor A burglary, Chancellor.

Chancellor Burglary, Majesty?

Emperor At the Royal Palace, Chancellor.

Chancellor The Palace, Majesty!

Emperor Before we go any further into the matter, Chancellor, you will oblige me by not repeating every word I say like a stuttering parrot.

The Chancellor bows low

And don't start all that business again! Listen to me! This afternoon, Chancellor, four thieves broke into the Royal Palace Vaults and stole four chests of gold. My gold, Chancellor.

Chancellor You don't say so, Majesty?

Emperor I have said so, haven't I, you burbling idiot! The four thieves, Chancellor, must be caught.

Chancellor Indeed they must, Majesty.

Emperor And when they are caught, Chancellor ... When they are caught—they must be punished.

Chancellor Indeed they must, Majesty. Might I suggest the Royal Dungeons?

Emperor Good, Chancellor. A good idea.

Chancellor Or—shall we say the Lower Dungeons, Majesty? The very Lowest Dungeons?

Emperor Warmer, Chancellor. You're getting warmer!

Chancellor Or even ... (*He draws a significant finger across his throat*)

Emperor Excellent, Chancellor! A capital suggestion!

Chancellor I am pleased your Majesty is pleased, your Majesty. And I can only venture to add that it is my most sincere desire that you should succeed in capturing the miscreants.

Emperor Chancellor ...

Chancellor Majesty?

Emperor I have a surprise for you, Chancellor. You are going to capture the thieves.

Chancellor I am?

Emperor You are. Or else ... (*He draws a significant finger across his throat*)

Chancellor Or else ... ? (*He imitates the gesture*)

Emperor Precisely.

Chancellor But, Majesty, if you don't mind, I would much rather turn down the assignment. You see, there are so many affairs of state to attend to and I did promise to ...

Emperor Chancellor! Self control! Remember! We don't want to lose our heads over this, do we?

Chancellor Indeed we don't, Majesty.

Emperor Good, good! I knew you'd listen to reason. Now then. Listen to me. I have already decided upon the plan you will follow. Two hours ago I instructed my Royal Astrologer to look in the heavens, study the stars, examine the skies and, in short, discover the whereabouts of the criminals. I ordered him to present me with their names, addresses, and all the usual particulars before sunset this afternoon.

Chancellor It is already sunset, Majesty.

Emperor I can see that, you oaf! Will you be quiet while I'm speaking! The Royal Astrologer, Chancellor, has failed.

Chancellor Most unfortunate.

Emperor (*taking a scroll from the wide sleeve of his robe*) As you remark, Chancellor. Most unfortunate. However, the possibility of the Royal Astrologer's failure in his appointed task did not altogether elude me. I have, in fact, prepared for that self-same contingency.

Chancellor Your Majesty thinks of everything.

Emperor Of course I do. (*He hands the scroll to the Chancellor*) What do you think of this, Chancellor?

Chancellor (*turning the scroll over in his hands*) It rather looks like ... like a scroll, Majesty.

Emperor Of course it looks like a scroll, Chancellor! It is a scroll!

Chancellor Why, so it is.

Emperor Be so good as to read it aloud, Chancellor!

The Chancellor opens the scroll, clears his throat and reads aloud in his most "official" voice

Chancellor "His Most Royal and Excellent Majesty, Indera Maya, on whose head may many blessings fall, (*he bows low*) requests the pleasure of the company of the Royal Court Astrologer at a public execution tomorrow. His own. Six o'clock sharp in the Palace grounds. No flowers by request."

Emperor How's that, Chancellor?

Chancellor Very beautifully put, if I may be permitted to say so, Majesty.

Emperor You will see that the order is carried out and then you must appoint a new Royal Astrologer. His task will be to discover the hiding place of the four thieves. Is that clear, Chancellor?

Chancellor Perfectly clear, Majesty.

Emperor Good.

Chancellor There would only appear to be one slight snag in the scheme, Majesty. I rather fear there are no further applicants for the post of Royal Astrologer. They don't seem to find the immediate prospects to their liking.

Emperor Nonsense, Chancellor! Absolute nonsense! The pay is good, isn't it?

Chancellor It is indeed, Majesty. But not one of the last six astrologers has managed to last until pay-day, Majesty.

Emperor You know, Chancellor, the trouble with these astrologers is that they lose their heads too quickly.

Chancellor Exactly, Majesty.

Emperor Most unfortunate, most unfortunate.

Chancellor (*re-rolling the scroll*) We can but persevere and keep on trying.

Emperor Exactly. Chancellor, you will despatch the Palace Messengers all over the kingdom. I want every astrologer, large or small, stout or slim, to present himself at the Royal Palace tomorrow afternoon.

Chancellor I shall deal with the matter personally.

Emperor Excellent, excellent! They shall all, each and every one, be given their chance to find the four thieves and my royal chests of gold.

Chancellor An admirable opportunity to test their separate skills.

Emperor Precisely. If one of them should succeed . . . If one of them should succeed, Chancellor, he will be appointed Royal Astrologer at the court of Indera Maya.

Chancellor An excellent idea, Majesty. And if I might be so bold as to suggest an added incentive . . .

Emperor What is it?

Chancellor Your daughter's hand in marriage.

Emperor The hand of the Princess!

Chancellor It's the usual custom.

Emperor My daughter marry a commoner!

Chancellor It's a very common practice.

Emperor The idea is unthinkable. Besides, no-one will ever marry the Princess. I gave up all hope years ago. She's all tantrums and tempers—I can't think who she takes after. Suitors take one look at her and take their leave.

Chancellor But if the Princess were part of the reward, Majesty, the winner would not dare refuse her.

Emperor Is there a punishment for refusing a royal reward, Chancellor?

Chancellor We could make one, Majesty.

Emperor And you think it might even assist in the recovery of my chests of gold?

Chancellor I do indeed, Majesty.

Emperor Very well. I agree.

Chancellor Your Majesty is too generous.

Emperor Far too generous, Chancellor. But then, one can only be what one is.

Chancellor And if they fail?

Emperor If they fail, Chancellor ... (*He draws his finger across his throat*)

The Chancellor repeats the gesture

Exactly. Also, yourself, Chancellor.

The Chancellor fingers his neck unhappily

But then, cheer up, Chancellor! Chin up, man! Chin up! After all—we don't *want* to lose our heads, do we?

Chancellor Most decidedly not, Majesty.

Emperor Well, off we go! I must get back to the palace. See that everything is in readiness for this astrologer competition tomorrow, eh, Chancellor? Joy, joy, joy! I do love entertainments! (*He crosses* R)

Chancellor But, Majesty, wait!

Emperor What is it now, Chancellor?

Chancellor All these people! (*He indicates the audience*) The play we promised! We can't just keep them waiting!

Emperor Play? People? What on earth are you babbling into your beard about now, Chancellor? Really, man! You must learn to think clearly! Or else, Chancellor ... Or else ... You follow me?

Chancellor I rather fear that I may precede you, your Majesty.

Emperor Excellent, Chancellor. Don't forget then. Tomorrow afternoon! All the astrologers!

Chancellor I shall deal with the matter immediately, Majesty. (*He bows out*)

The Emperor exits R

The Chancellor crosses downstage and again addresses the audience

I might have guessed that something like this would happen. And to think, only this morning, I had everything perfectly organized. And now this! First the Emperor is lost and the Palace is burgled and I ... I shall lose my head, that's easy to see. I do need time to think. You may wait if you wish—I'm sure we'll be able to sort something out later. For the time being—I must compose my mind to the matter in hand (*He turns to exit*)

Father Mole-Cricket enters through the house door and crosses down the veranda. He is carrying a large sign-board

In his haste the Chancellor bumps into Father Mole-Cricket. He brushes him aside with a gesture of annoyance

Out of the way, my good fellow! I must have time to think!

Father Mole-Cricket puts down his sign, scratches his head and watches as:

The Chancellor exits

The house door opens and Mother Mole-Cricket enters

She crosses down to watch her husband as he turns the sign around for the audience to see. In large letters is written: "FATHER MOLE CRICKET. ASTROLOGER". Father Mole-Cricket steps back to admire the sign

Mother Mole-Cricket Astrologer indeed! What nonsense!

Father Mole-Cricket You may scoff, my dear, but just you wait and see. Who knows—someday I may be as famous as the Royal Astrologer himself! ... Yes, as famous as the Royal Court Astrologer ...

Mother Mole-Cricket shrugs her shoulders in despair and exits into the house

Father Mole-Cricket stands admiring the sign as——

—*the* CURTAIN *falls*

SCENE 2

The same. Later the same evening

The Chancellor looking rather bedraggled, enters R. *He is limping and mopping his brow with a large handkerchief. He crosses downstage and lowers himself carefully onto the grass. He again mops his forehead and proceeds to remove his shoes from which he extracts a stone. He replaces the shoe, examines the stone, and addresses the audience*

Chancellor Oh, that's better! Much better! That stone has been working its way from my heel to my toe and toe to heel for the last mile at least. I've never walked so far in so short a time in all my life—nothing like it. Thank goodness you're still here, at any rate. I thought, perhaps, you'd have all gone home by now. It's this business with the Emperor. So annoying! And such a temper! (*He rubs his left leg tenderly*) Excuse me a moment. Now my foot's gone to sleep. And I ache—oh, how I ache! I just am not used to all this walking ... (*He massages his shin gently*) Oh, that's better. Yes, now I can waggle my toes again. Where was I? The play! I hadn't forgotten, you see. But honestly! What chance have I had? Do you know, I've walked all the way to the next village and back since I saw you last? Do you know why? Because I'm looking for astrologers! Looking for astrologers! There's an errand if you please! And in all that distance, do you know how many astrologers I've found? ... Guess. Go on—guess! You can't, can you? Very well, I'll tell you. Not one. No, not a solitary astrologer in six miles at least. And it's no joke I don't mind telling you. Because if I don't find one, do you know what's going to happen? This. (*He draws his finger across his throat*) Well, there's gratitude for you. Is it my fault if there aren't any astrologers? Is it? Of course it isn't! Well, one thing's certain—if we can't have an astrologer, at least we can have a play. Where were we? Just a minute ... (*He struggles to his feet*) You'll never know how much better I feel for that short rest. We did start here, didn't we? Yes—same garden—same house. Good. (*He looks around the garden and, for the first time, notices the sign*) Hullo! What's this! Do you know, I could swear that wasn't there the last time we started. (*He crosses to examine the sign*) Well, just look here! What do you make of this! Forgive me a moment. (*He takes out a pair of spectacles, puts them on, and reads the wording under his breath. He takes off the spectacles, replaces them in his robes and turns to the audience*) Father Mole-Cricket—Astrologer. Well, if that doesn't beat everything I don't know what does. There and back I've been and here's one right under my very nose. (*He takes out a notebook and pencil and writes down the name*) Father . . . Mole . . . Cricket . . . Funny sort of name for an astrologer, but that can't be helped. I must get back to the Palace with this at once. ... Look, I'm terribly sorry to have to leave you again—but you do understand. This could be a matter of life or death for me. (*He replaces the notebook and pencil in his robes*) Don't go away. I do promise to come back as soon as I can and we'll start where we left off. That's a promise. (*He turns to exit*)

Father Mole-Cricket enters through the house door carrying a large bowl of onions. He seats himself on the veranda as the Chancellor crosses to speak to him

This could be the astrologer himself. I'll have a word with him. (*To Father Mole-Cricket*) Good-evening!

Father Mole-Cricket (*looking up from his task and noticing the Chancellor*) Oh! Why, a very good evening to you too, your worshipful Eminence.

Chancellor Indeed it is! It is indeed! In fact, it's a beautiful evening!

Father Mole-Cricket I'm sure I'm happy to find you enjoying it.

Chancellor Oh—but will you believe me when I tell you that, less than two minutes ago, I had no eyes whatsoever for the excellence of the night air?

Father Mole-Cricket Is that a fact, your Honour! Well, now! Think of that ... Er ... You'll excuse me, I hope, if I carry on with this task my wife has set me?

Chancellor Carry on, good sir! By all means! Pay no attention to me. Pray don't allow my small talk to disturb you in your duties.

Father Mole-Cricket Thanks very much. It isn't that I want to do it, you understand. It isn't that I wouldn't far rather have a little talk with you. It's my wife, you know.

Chancellor Don't trouble to explain. I fully understand. Wait! Don't tell me! Let me guess!

Father Mole-Cricket pauses to wipe away a tear

You're peeling onions!

Father Mole-Cricket Indeed I am, your Highness.

Chancellor And what excellent onions!

Father Mole-Cricket Are they? They are? I don't know—they look—more or less—like any kind of onions to me. Leastways, that's how they smell.

Chancellor Not at all. I might say that those are the finest onions I have seen in a long, long time.

Father Mole-Cricket Might you really, sir?

Chancellor I will say it! They are the finest onions I have seen in a long, long time!

Father Mole-Cricket (*putting down the bowl and examining the contents with a new interest*) Is that a fact? Oh. You'll ... you'll ... er ... pardon me making the inquiry, your Excellency, but was there something you were wanting?

Chancellor No, no! I just happened to be passing through the village, and I ... well I decided to spend a few moments in your delightful garden.

Father Mole-Cricket Delightful? Do you really think so? Always seemed like any other back garden to me. I never seem to be able to get round and tidy it up.

Chancellor Tidy it up? But, why? As soon as I arrived I was immediately taken with its ... its neatness and ... and its general air of ... well-being.

Father Mole-Cricket Fancy now!

Chancellor To say nothing of the rustic charm.

Father Mole-Cricket Is that a fact!

Chancellor You'll pardon the question, but your name wouldn't, by any chance, be Mole-Cricket?

Father Mole-Cricket However did you guess!

Chancellor Is it really? And not ... No. No, it couldn't be ...

Father Mole-Cricket What's that?

Chancellor Nothing. Just an idle, foolish fancy of my own. It isn't possible, of course, but I was wondering whether you might, perhaps, be *Father* Mole-Cricket?

Father Mole-Cricket Somebody must have told you.

Chancellor Or should I say, Father Mole-Cricket, the celebrated astrologer?

Father Mole-Cricket The celebrated ... Oh no. No, you'll pardon me venturing to contradict an important personage same as yourself—but, no. Not celebrated. Just a beginner, your Importanceship. Only a mere beginner.

Chancellor But you are an astrologer?

Father Mole-Cricket In a small sort of way.

Chancellor Wonderful, wonderful! It couldn't be better.

Father Mole-Cricket Was there ... was there something your Majestance was wanting? A little bit of astrologizing, perhaps? It is normal to make

an appointment but, as you can see, I'm not very busy this evening
and——

Chancellor No, thank you. Nothing at all. It's quite all right. I was just
passing. An astrologer! What luck! How wonderful! And now, if you'll
forgive me, I'll be on my way. Good-day to you, Father Mole-Cricket. It's
been a pleasure to hear of your existence. A true pleasure. (*He moves off* R)

Father Mole-Cricket (*scratching his head*) Good-bye, sir I'm only too
pleased to have met you, too.

Chancellor Not good-bye, Father Mole-Cricket! I'm quite sure we will meet
again. (*To himself*) A real astrologer! A real genuine astrologer! Oh, the
Emperor will be pleased!

He exits R

Father Mole-Cricket (*again taking up the bowl of onions*) Strange! Most
peculiar! What an odd sort of man! Still . . . we get all kinds round these
parts . . . (*He shakes his head as he takes another onion from the bowl and
begins to peel it*)

Master Mole-Cricket, very much out of breath, enters R *and crosses to his
father's side*

Master Mole-Cricket Father! Father! . . . Father! . . . It worked, Father!
Just like you said!

Father Mole-Cricket You hid the buffaloes, my boy?

Master Mole-Cricket That I did, Father! I waited in the long grass until the
villagers were busy at the other end of the rice-fields. And then I took the
buffaloes and hid them in the bushes beyond the village, just as you told
me. And then . . . and then I went back to the fields.

Father Mole-Cricket And then?

Master Mole-Cricket By then the villagers were in a terrible state. Searching
all over. High and low. They were very put out, I can tell you.

Father Mole-Cricket And then?

Master Mole-Cricket And then I told them you were an astri . . . astor . . .
astro . . .

Father Mole-Cricket Ologer?

Master Mole-Cricket Yes. Well, then they all started talking at once. You
never heard anything like it. They were shouting and arguing so loudly
that it took me all my time to get a word in.

Father Mole-Cricket Yes, my boy. Go on, go on.

Master Mole-Cricket But I managed to tell them that you might be able to
help them, by looking in the stars and so on.

Father Mole-Cricket Yes, yes!

Master Mole-Cricket And then they decided to send a depu . . . a depu . . . a
depu . . .

Father Mole-Cricket Tation?

Master Mole-Cricket That's it. A deputation. They decided to send a
deputation to see you. They're on their way here now. I had to run all the
way back to get here first—and very tired it's made me feel, I don't mind

telling you. I'm just about ready for a good, long sleep. So if you'll excuse
me, I'll ... (*He yawns and stretches*)

Father Mole-Cricket (*rising*) On their way now! Then we must hurry, my
boy! Come along, come along! This is no time for going to sleep. We have
work to do.

Master Mole-Cricket But, Father ...

Father Mole-Cricket Do as I say, son! There isn't a minute to spare. Here!
(*He hands the bowl of onions to his son*) Take these into the house and
bring me out that old telescope which belonged to my late great-uncle, the
Admiral of the Fleet.

Master Mole-Cricket Telescope, Father? I don't see why ...

Father Mole-Cricket Quickly now! Do as I say.

Master Mole-Cricket (*crossing up on to veranda*) Oh, very well, Father ...
Very well ... I'm going ...

Master Mole-Cricket exits through the door into the house

*Father Mole-Cricket smooths his clothes and excitedly trots down to place the
sign in a more prominent position. He returns to the veranda*

*Master Mole-Cricket enters, carrying in his arms an ancient and battered
telescope which he hands to his father. They seat themselves on the steps of
the veranda*

The Villagers shuffle hesitantly on from the right

*The spokesman of the pair, the First Villager, is uncommonly tall, the Second
Villager is uncommonly short. If the cast is sufficiently large other Villagers
should follow the deputation at a respectable distance—but if these are
unavailable they can be dispensed with. The two Villagers move slowly across
to where the two Mole-Crickets are seated*

First Villager Good-evening, Father Mole-Cricket!

Second Villager Indeed, a very good evening to you, Father Mole-Cricket!

*Father Mole-Cricket has been carefully examining the telescope and now
looks up*

Father Mole-Cricket Well, well, well! This is a pleasant surprise, neighbours! But how hot you look! And tired. Don't they look hot, my son?

Master Mole-Cricket Hot and tired, Father. Just like you said.

Father Mole-Cricket But then, of course, you've been in the fields all day,
haven't you?

First Villager Indeed we have, Father Mole-Cricket.

Second Villager We have indeed, Father Mole-Cricket.

First Villager Since daybreak this morning. Tending and tilling our crops
since cock-crow.

Second Villager The very first cock-crow.

Father Mole-Cricket Dear me, dear me! But sit down, friends. Please make
yourselves comfortable!

*The two Villagers seat themselves on the grass at the feet of Father Mole-
Cricket*

That's better! Much better! Now, perhaps you will tell me what it is that I can do for you? Or have you just called to while away the hours and pass the time of day?

First Villager That we haven't, Father Mole-Cricket!

Second Villager Indeed we haven't, Father Mole-Cricket!

First Villager We've no time for gossip!

Second Villager None at all!

First Villager We came for advice.

Second Villager That's right. Advice.

Father Mole-Cricket No time for gossip? Dear me, that is a sorry state of affairs. But if it is advice you're seeking—and if I am able to give it—why then, it's yours for the asking. But, to come to me for advice? Wasn't it yourself who called me a lazy old fool? And only last week at that?

First Villager A lazy old fool, Father Mole-Cricket? Indeed I did not!

Second Villager Indeed he did not!

First Villager Why, I was saying, only last week, what a wise and clever person you were. Wasn't I, neighbours?

Second Villager Wise and clever. Those were your very words.

First Villager And hard working. Didn't I say, "hard-working", neighbour?

Second Villager That you did, neighbour! That you certainly did. I remember it most distinctly. Hard-working.

First Villager Definitely, hard-working, wise and clever.

Father Mole-Cricket Well now! What do you say to that, my boy? All those nice things our good neighbours have been saying about me! Wise and . . . and . . .

Master Mole-Cricket Clever, Father.

Father Mole-Cricket Yes, clever. Wise and clever and . . . and . . .

First Villager Hard-working, Father Mole-Cricket.

Father Mole-Cricket Wise and clever and hard-working! I shall be very pleased to give you any advice that I can. What was it you wished to know?

First Villager We have heard that you are an astrologer, Father Mole-Cricket.

Second Villager That's just what we heard.

Father Mole-Cricket Mmmmm. Well . . . yes, I have studied a little.

First Villager We have lost two of our best buffaloes, Father Mole-Cricket.

Second Villager Our very best buffaloes.

First Villager Gone from under our very noses.

Second Villager That's just how they went.

First Villager The strongest buffaloes in the whole country.

Second Villager In all the land.

First Villager Vanished—that's what they've done.

Second Villager Vanished . . .

First Villager And we thought, perhaps, with all your learning . . .

Second Villager Learning . . .

First Villager You might be able to help us find them . . .

Second Villager Find them . . .

First Villager If you have the time, that is . . .

Second Villager Oh, indeed, only if you have the time, Father Mole-Cricket.
Father Mole-Cricket Buffaloes ... Oh, dear! ... Buffaloes!
First Villager Is ... Is anything wrong, Father Mole-Cricket? We would be
willing to reward you most handsomely if only you could help us.
Second Villager If only you *could* help us, Father Mole-Cricket!
Father Mole-Cricket That's very kind of you, neighbours. But, you see, the
fact is—I haven't got as far as buffaloes in my studies. Now, if they had
been white rabbits, say—or guinea pigs ... Do you know, I was only
learning how to find guinea pigs last night. And as for white rabbits! Why,
I could find you a couple of white rabbits as easy as look at you ... But
buffaloes ... (*He shakes his head*) I don't know the first thing about
buffaloes. You wouldn't care to lose some white rabbits, would you?
First Villager Couldn't you just *try* buffaloes?
Second Villager Yes, could you just *try* buffaloes, Father Mole-Cricket?
Father Mole-Cricket I don't really think ...
First Villager We would be most grateful ...
Second Villager *Most* grateful ...
Father Mole-Cricket Very well! You're both good friends of mine and, all
things considered, I will try.
First Villager Thank you very much, Father Mole-Cricket!
Second Villager Very much indeed, Father Mole-Cricket.
Father Mole-Cricket Pass me my spectacles, my boy.

Master Mole-Cricket hands his father an ornate pair of spectacles

Good! Now for my telescope.

*He examines the telescope, squints through it, blows down it and a cloud of
dust drifts out of the end and sends the Villagers into bursts of coughing*

And now, I shall examine the skies.

*Father Mole-Cricket peers at the sky through his telescope. The Villagers
watch anxiously*

Yes ... yes. ... You did say buffaloes, didn't you?
First Villager Indeed we did, Father Mole-Cricket.
Second Villager We did indeed!
Father Mole-Cricket Good. That's what I thought you said, but I just
wanted to make sure. (*He returns to his study of the skies*) Well, well,
well! ... Goodness me! ...
First Villager What can you see in the skies, Father Mole-Cricket?
Second Villager Yes. Tell us what the skies say.
Father Mole-Cricket The skies say that if you search in the bushes, just past
the village, you may find what you are seeking ...

*Unnoticed by Father Mole-Cricket the two Villagers make a hasty and
joyful exit*

But I don't promise anything ... Now, if they had been white rabbits ...
(*He lowers the telescope*) Gracious me! They've gone! (*He crosses down
into the garden*)

Master Mole-Cricket (*following his father*) What do we do next, Father?

Father Mole-Cricket Now, my boy, we wait for our good friends, the villagers, to find the buffaloes.

Master Mole-Cricket And then?

Father Mole-Cricket Why—then we collect our reward.

Master Mole-Cricket (*yawning*) I suppose that will take about an hour, Father?

Father Mole-Cricket An hour, at the very least, my son.

Master Mole-Cricket One can have a fine sleep in an hour . . .

Father Mole-Cricket Exactly what I was thinking myself, my boy . . .

Master Mole-Cricket (*selecting a shady spot in the garden*) A . . . very fine sleep indeed . . .

The Palace Messenger enters R. *He is wearing an uncomfortable collection of armour and carries a large sword at his waist*

Father Mole-Cricket Just a moment, son, it seems as we have a visitor!

Master Mole-Cricket He isn't one of the villagers, Father. And, if you ask me, he doesn't look as if he might be interested in astrology. I'd say, he looks rather fierce.

The Palace Messenger looks around uncertainly before he sees the two Mole-Crickets who are vainly attempting to hide behind the sign-board

Messenger Evening!

Father Mole-Cricket Leave this to me, my boy.

The Mole-Crickets venture out from behind the sign

Good-evening to you too, sir. And a very fine evening it is, if you don't mind me saying so.

Messenger Perhaps it is for some—then again, perhaps it isn't for others.

Father Mole-Cricket A matter of taste, I suppose?

Messenger If you was to ask my opinion, I'd say it was hot. Terrible hot.

Father Mole-Cricket You might say it was a trifle warm.

Messenger Warm? It's hot. Terrible hot. (*He mops his forehead*)

Father Mole-Cricket I suppose that's because you've been doing a lot of walking. Now, if you want my advice, I'd suggest that you lie down here in the shade for a few minutes. You'd feel much better for it, I can assure you.

Messenger Lie down! Me—lie down! On duty! That's a good one, that is! I wouldn't like to think what his Majesty would have to say about that!

Father Mole-Cricket His Majesty?

Messenger The Emperor. Indera Maya. (*Proudly*) I'm his special messenger.

Father Mole-Cricket That must be a very important position!

Messenger Terrible important. Ask me, I'd say it was one of the most important positions what is—speaking offhand, like.

Master Mole-Cricket Of course.

Father Mole-Cricket And very interesting work, too, I should imagine?

Messenger Ah! Now that would depend on how important is the message I would happen to be carrying at the time of asking.

Father Mole-Cricket I can understand that.

Messenger (*approaching to speak in closer confidence*) Now, take today for instance. I've got a terrible important message with me right now.

Father Mole-Cricket Have you really?

Messenger What! Why, I reckon this must be one of the most important messages that ever was.

Father Mole-Cricket No!

Messenger Indeed yes. I might easily get made corporal for this. See—I've got to find a party. Name of Bucket.

Father Mole-Cricket Bucket?

Messenger Father Coal-Bucket.

Master Mole-Cricket Mole-Cricket?

Messenger Know him, do you?

Father Mole-Cricket Well, er . . . What do you want him for?

Messenger Not me—it's the Emperor. Terrible temper he was in when I left.

Father Mole-Cricket Indera Maya?

Messenger Terrible temper. Horrible. Fair falling over themselves up at that palace. You . . . er . . . You wouldn't know where I might be able to lay my hands on this here Father Coat-Pocket, would you?

Father Mole-Cricket I'm afraid not. Would we, my boy?

Master Mole-Cricket Most decidedly not, Father.

Messenger Pity that. See, if I had to walk all the way back to the Palace, getting terrible hot, then find I had to walk all the way back here, getting terrible hotter, all because someone had told me an untruth—I wouldn't very much care to be in that someone's shoes. If you see what I mean. Me being hasty with my temper, so to speak.

Father Mole-Cricket Really?

Messenger Oh, terrible hasty my temper is—especially when I'm hot.

Father Mole-Cricket I see.

Messenger (*drawing his sword*) I . . . I, er . . . brought my sword with me. (*He sweeps, idly, at the blades of grass*)

Father Mole-Cricket So I see. Is it . . . sharp?

Messenger (*running his thumb cautiously down the blade*) Terrible sharp. Like to feel?

Father Mole-Cricket No, thank you very much. What was the message?

Messenger Your name Gasket?

Father Mole-Cricket Cricket. Mole-Cricket. Father Mole-Cricket.

Messenger That's better. I've got it here somewhere. Terrible important this message is. I reckon there can't be all that many messages as important as this one is.

Father Mole-Cricket But what does it say?

Messenger Half a tick. I'm coming to that. I've got it here somewhere . . . Now, where did I put it? . . . Well, I know I had it when I left the Palace, that's a fact. . . . Very important this message is. (*He feels from pocket to pocket without success. The cold horror of losing the message steals across* *his face as his searchings prove fruitless. Suddenly he smiles. He removes his helmet and takes out a scroll)* Here we are! I'll read it out shall I?

Father Mole-Cricket If you would be so kind.

Messenger *(opening the scroll)* This is it, then. The message. *(He clears his throat)* "His Most Gracious Majesty, Indera Maya, extends his heartfelt greetings and good wishes to his loyal subject, Father Mole-Cricket (that's you), and hereby requests the pleasure of the company of the above-named loyal subject at an ... at an ... astor ... astra ... astar ..." *(He passes the scroll across to Father Mole-Cricket)* What's that word there?

Father Mole-Cricket Astrologer.

Messenger Thanks very much. "At an astrologer competition tomorrow afternoon in the Royal Palace. Two-thirty sharp." That's the message.

Father Mole-Cricket Oh. Well, of course, it's more than kind of his Majesty to invite me. But you see, I've had a rather busy day, and I do feel rather tired. So if you'd just go back and explain to——

Messenger Half a tick. There's a bit more at the bottom here that I forgot to read out the last time. "Failure to comply with this order will be punishable by ... by ... exe ... exor ... exas" ... *(He again passes the scroll over)*

Father Mole-Cricket Execution.

Messenger *(re-examining the scroll)* Why, so it is! Bit of bad writing that is. Execution. That means he'll chop off your head if you don't turn up.

Father Mole-Cricket I know.

Messenger Always was the one for big words was the Emperor. Execution! It's a good one that is, isn't it? Execution! Ex-ee-cue-shun!

Father Mole-Cricket Did you say two-thirty?

Messenger Sharp.

Father Mole-Cricket We'll set off at once. Come along, my boy.

Messenger Who's he?

Father Mole-Cricket My assistant.

Master Mole-Cricket Me, Father? But I was going to ...

Father Mole-Cricket I said, come along!

Master Mole-Cricket Very well, Father, I'm coming ... I'm coming!

Messenger Hurry up, then! I haven't got all night, you know.

Father Mole-Cricket We're ready.

They move across the stage, R. The Messenger, carrying his sword, leads the way. He is followed by Father Mole-Cricket, who is carrying the telescope. Master Mole-Cricket trails in the rear

Mother Mole-Cricket enters through the house door

Mother Mole-Cricket Husband! ... Husband! When are you going to finish ... *(She sees the small procession)* And where do you think you're going?

Father Mole-Cricket *(pausing)* I'm sorry, my love, I can't stop now. I'm wanted at the Emperor's Palace. I'll see you tomorrow ... I hope.

Messenger Are you coming, or aren't you?

Father Mole-Cricket Lead the way!

Mother Mole-Cricket (*crossing down from veranda*) Yes ... but ... Just a
minute ... Just a minute ...

*The Messenger, Father Mole-Cricket and Master Mole-Cricket march
off,* R

*Mother Mole-Cricket stands, hands on hips, and watches them move out of
sight*

Astrology! ... Emperor's Palace! ... Telescopes! ... Such nonsense!
Who's going to finish peeling the onions? That's what I'd like to know.

Mother Mole-Cricket is returning to the house as——

the CURTAIN *falls*

SCENE 3

The Palace of Indera Maya. The following afternoon

Before the CURTAIN *rises the Chancellor, carrying a long scroll, enters and
addresses the audience across the "footlights"*

Chancellor Worse and worse. Everything is going wrong! I give up. I
absolutely and finally give up! You have my sympathy, but what more
can I do than assure you that all of this is none of my doing. I'm sorry to
have to tell you that, as far as I can see, there isn't the slightest chance of
our being ready to start the play for a month at least. That's the honest
truth and I can't speak fairer than that. Do you know what's going on
behind there? (*He indicates the curtain*) I'll tell you. The competition. Do
you know how long it's been going on now? Three hours. All afternoon.
Do you know what this is? (*He holds up the scroll*) This—believe it or
not—this is the list of the competitors' names! Look! (*He allows the scroll
to unroll—it very nearly reaches the ground*) Now you see the position
we're in. And that's not all. Listen. (*He drops his voice and speaks
confidentially*). You'd think that even the fools we have for palace
messengers would be able to understand a straightforward order. You'd
be wrong. They can't. Go out, they were told, go out and bring back all
the astrologers in the kingdom. Well, that's simple enough, isn't it? Can
you guess what these idiots have done? I'll tell you. They not only bring
back all the astrologers, they also turn up with every wizard, magician,
conjuror and card-sharper from here to Peking. Oh, if you only knew the
trouble I've had with them today! The spells that have been cast in this
Palace are nobody's business. It's going to take us a week, at least, to get
rid of the smell of flash paper. We even had one ill-mannered lout who
spent the whole of two hours pulling eggs from the cook's mouth. Is it my
fault, then, if the good woman packs her bags and walks out? As for the
Princess—she, poor girl, has taken one look at the collection of doddering

decrepits and gangling greybeards assembled here today and has not spoken one word since. His Majesty is furious. And for all the tricks and wands and wizardry of these so-called magicians, do you think there is one single one of them who can do a simple thing such as find four missing chests of gold? Not on your life. Not one.

Emperor (*calling; off*) Chancellor! . . . Chancellor!

Chancellor I'm coming, your Majesty! You see? He's been like that all day. Chancellor here—Chancellor there. Chancellor—do this. Chancellor—do that.

Emperor (*calling; off*) Chancellor!!

Chancellor Coming, Majesty! I shall have to see what he wants. You good people can stay or go—just as you please. As I've said already—I give up. Curtain, please!

The CURTAIN *begins to rise. It is about two feet from the ground when the Chancellor puts out his hand to stay its progress*

Wait! . . . Before I go I would like to state, categorically, here and now, that never, as long as I live, do I want to hear the word "astrologer" again. Thank you.

He motions to the CURTAIN *which, again, begins to rise. The* CURTAIN *goes up and we are in the Throne Room of the Emperor*

Here I am, Majesty. Here I am!

The Emperor is seated L *on a large and ornate throne. The Princess is seated next to her father on a similar, though somewhat smaller throne. She sits with her arms folded and is obviously in a "temper"*

An unhappy competitor, the Wizard, is standing DR, *and performing his mystical rites with a crystal ball, which is placed on a small oriental table. He is dressed in the manner of the usual 'fairy-tale' version of a wizard: long cloak and conical hat covered with the signs of the zodiac. He is very old and has a long grey beard. He is peering into the crystal agitatedly and muttering strange incantations. He pauses in his task occasionally to rub the crystal with a bright yellow duster*

On either side of him stands a large, threatening, Palace Guard

Emperor There you are, Chancellor! Where on earth have you been, man?

Chancellor My deepest and most humble apologies, Majesty. I rather fear that I had some important business to attend to.

Emperor Business, business! What business, Chancellor? Your business is to attend to me! Here I've had to sit for the last ten minutes, listening to the droning dirge of this doddering imbecile! Well, it won't do, Chancellor! Who is he anyway? Do you realise, Chancellor, that this one is the worst of the whole bunch?

Chancellor (*thumbing down the list of names*) This is competitor number seventy-three, Majesty, He is entered on the list as a Wizard and Astrologer—from one of your Majesty's lesser-known provinces.

Emperor Then we can only hope, Chancellor, that we never have to hear of it again.

Chancellor He is held, I believe, in high esteem in his own district. He also has a remarkable record for finding things . . .

Emperor Good. Then tell him to find his way to the Royal Execution Chamber.

Chancellor If your Majesty would only give him time. You may be interested to hear that he claims descent from a long line of astrologers beginning with——

Emperor (*rising*) My Majesty will not be interested to hear what he claims! Look here, Chancellor, all afternoon I've been watching one bungling idiot after another performing paltry parlour tricks until I'm sick to death of the sight of them. I would remind you, Chancellor, that we are also in search of a suitable subject for my daughter's hand. She was difficult enough to deal with before this business started, but now . . . now she's impossible. She refuses to speak to me. Utterly refuses. Me! Her father! (*He turns to the Princess*) Don't you refuse to speak to me?

The Princess tosses her head

You see? She refuses. But of all the fossilized old freaks you've allowed to enter this room today, Chancellor, this one takes the bun.

Chancellor The biscuit, Majesty.

Emperor What's that?

Chancellor I believe you mean that he takes the biscuit.

Emperor Biscuits? Boxes of biscuits? Who said anything about biscuits? We are gathered here today, Chancellor, I might remind you, to discover the whereabouts of my missing chests of gold. If you have nothing more to offer in the way of help, but to stand there, mumbling through your moustache about boxes of biscuits, I feel that we'd all be a lot better off with you out of the way for a start.

Chancellor I shall apply myself to the task in hand at once, Majesty.

Emperor Just see that you do. All I wish to know is, can he or can't he tell me where to find the chests of gold? If he can, why doesn't he? And if he can't why doesn't he say so, instead of standing there, waving his arms in the air and wasting all our time? (*He crosses* R)

The Wizard, who has paused in his mysterious passes, has turned and is furtively listening to the conversation

Come along, man! Get on with it! You are an astrologer, aren't you? That's what he is, isn't he, Chancellor?

Chancellor Indeed he is, Majesty.

Wizard Indeed I am, Majesty.

Emperor Well then, astrologize! All I want to know is who has stolen my four chests of gold.

Wizard If you will be so kind as to allow me time . . . (*He again applies himself to the crystal ball*) Abracadabra, abracadabra, hokum, pokum, mystical ball . . .

Emperor And do stop burbling in that idiotic language! I can't understand a word you say. Can you tell me what he's saying, Chancellor?

Chancellor I must admit, Majesty, that I find it difficult to decipher the decidedly foreign element in——

Emperor Oh shut up! You're worse than he is! Will you get on with it, man!

Wizard (*applying himself diligently to his task*) Abradacabra, abracadabra, abracadabra ...

The Wizard's head bends lower and lower over the crystal. Interestedly, the heads of the Emperor, the Chancellor and the two Guards follow suit. The Wizard drones on

Abracadabra, hokum, pokum, icarum, ticarum, raaaaaaaaaa ...

Emperor }
Chancellor } (*hopefully*) Aaaaah?

Wizard Er ... no.

The Emperor lifts his head in annoyance. Unfortunately the Chancellor does the same. Their heads crash together

Abracadabra, abracadabra——

Emperor Stop! I refuse to listen a moment longer to this nonsense! Guards.

The Emperor points dramatically off

    The Guards, one at either end, pick up the table and, followed by a still incantating Wizard waving his arms above the crystal ball, exit L in double time

Who's next, Chancellor?

The Chancellor crosses the Wizard's name from the list and again thumbs down

Chancellor I am sorry to have to inform your Majesty that we would appear to have exhausted the entire body of applicants.

Emperor (*pacing up and down the room*) Really, Chancellor! It's too bad! It won't do! Not one astrologer in all my kingdom to carry out a simple task such as this? To find four chests of gold! Why, it's the kind of thing that any star-gazer worth his salt would be glad to jump at. It isn't fair, Chancellor! Other emperors can find capable astrologers—where's mine?

Chancellor The whole of the countryside has been searched, Majesty. You have already, this afternoon ... er ... interviewed three hundred and eighty-nine competitors.

Emperor Three hundred and eighty-nine! As many as that, Chancellor?

Chancellor Three hundred and eighty-nine exactly. It would appear that the astrologers in your Majesty's lands do not possess the heads for the job.

Emperor Not any longer, Chancellor.

Chancellor No, Majesty. It is most unfortunate.

Emperor Precisely, Chancellor. As you say, most unfortunate.

The Chancellor bows low

For you.

Chancellor Me, Majesty?

Emperor You, Chancellor. (*He draws his finger across his throat*) Remember?

Chancellor I do indeed, Majesty.

Emperor What an excellent memory you have! And now, if you'll be so good, Chancellor, as to trot along to the Royal Execution Chamber and present yourself with my compliments to the Head Executioner . . .

Chancellor The . . . Head Executioner, Majesty?

Emperor I'm sure he'll be very pleased to see you. You'll be able to talk together, Chancellor, as one head to another, eh? (*He laughs uproariously*) I have made a joke, Chancellor. Be so good as to laugh.

Chancellor (*weakly*) Ha-ha. (*He takes a handkerchief from his robes in order to mop his brow. As he shakes the handkerchief open his notebook falls to the floor*) Majesty! We have one more chance!

Emperor Eh?

Chancellor (*stooping and picking up the notebook*) And to think that I almost forgot.

Emperor Speak clearly, Chancellor! What are you muttering about now?

Chancellor There is one more astrologer left! (*He flicks through the pages of the notebook hastily*) I found him myself yesterday.

Emperor You did, Chancellor?

Chancellor (*locating the page*) Here we are—Father Mole-Cricket. A rather common fellow, I am afraid, Majesty.

Emperor We can but try, Chancellor. We can do no more than try.

Chancellor I will have him summoned into your Majesty's presence immediately.

Emperor Please do, Chancellor. And while you're about it, you might tell the executioner to sharpen his axe.

Chancellor Sharpen it, Majesty?

Emperor (*returning to his throne*) Always expect the best, Chancellor, but be prepared for the worst.

Chancellor How very true. How very, very true. With your permission?

The Emperor inclines his head

(*Clapping his hands*) Summon Father Mole-Cricket!

First Voice (*off*) His Most Royal Majesty, Indera Maya, desires audience with Father Mole-Cricket!

Second Voice (*farther off*) His Most Royal Majesty, Indera Maya, desires audience with Father Mole-Cricket. . . . Father Mole-Cricket for audience with His Most Royal Majesty, Indera Maya.

First Voice (*off*) Father Mole-Cricket for audience with His Most Royal Majesty, Indera Maya!

A gong booms loudly off

The Emperor has been fidgeting on his throne during the above announcements. At the sound of the gong he claps his hands to his ears

Emperor Whose idea was all that nonsense, Chancellor?

Chancellor Nonsense, Majesty?

Emperor You heard what I said. All that shouting and gonging nonsense!

Father Mole-Cricket and Master Mole-Cricket shuffle into the Throne Room and prostrate themselves before the Emperor

Chancellor That's the latest order of the Keeper of your Royal Majesty's Household.

Emperor It's the last order of the Keeper of My Majesty's Household.

Chancellor Execution, Majesty?

Emperor Precisely.

Chancellor Tomorrow, Majesty?

Emperor Exactly.

Chancellor Dawn, Majesty?

Emperor Sharp.

Chancellor (*bowing low*) I shall attend to it personally. (*He crosses to stand* L *of the Emperor's throne*)

Emperor You, I take it, are Socket?

Father Mole-Cricket (*still kow-towing*) Cricket, Majesty. Mole-Cricket.

Emperor All right, Sticket, all right, you can stop that business. Stand up, man! Get up! Let me look at you.

The Two Mole-Crickets clamber cautiously to their feet

Well, Rocket, what have you got to say for yourself? And who is this you have with you, eh?

Father Mole-Cricket My son, Majesty. My assistant astrologer.

Emperor Assistant astrologer, eh?

Master Mole-Cricket Indeed I am, Majesty.

Emperor Assistants? I don't remember inviting any assistants to the competition. Was there anything in the rules about it, Chancellor?

Chancellor No, Majesty.

Emperor Then we can't allow it, can we?

Chancellor No, Majesty. Although, if I may be so bold as to point out to your Royal Majesty, there is a certain modicum of sound sense in the old saying—two heads are better than one.

Emperor Two heads are better than ... Chancellor! Now you've made a joke! Excellent, excellent! Laugh, Wicket, laugh, man!

The Mole-Crickets laugh feebly

Oh, very good, Chancellor! Yes, I feel that under the circumstances, your assistant may remain, Jacket.

The two Mole-Crickets bow

You will no doubt be pleased to hear that the other competitors have failed, Tisket.

Father Mole-Cricket Failed, Majesty?

The Emperor climbs down from his throne and walks around the Mole-Crickets as he speaks. They watch him apprehensively

Emperor Failed, Tasket. Yes. They were hardly suitable. Unfortunately they were all rather nervous men. Eh, Chancellor?

Chancellor Indeed they were, Majesty. Very nervous. I believe the expression is ... er ... highly strung.

Emperor True, Chancellor. In fact, Rocket, they were strung up. (*He laughs again*) I hope Biscuit, that you are not highly strung, because if you are not successful, we shall have to say that you are no astrologer—and then there will be – no astrologer—eh, Chancellor?

Chancellor How true, Majesty.

Emperor To put it plainly, Basket, the punishment for wasting my time is death, Cutlet.

Father Mole-Cricket Death, Majesty?

Emperor Death, Omelette. After a fair trial, of course. If you do fail you must be punished, you understand that, of course?

Father Mole-Cricket That's exactly what I said to the messenger. "I shall only be wasting his Majesty's valuable time," I said. Didn't I, my boy?

Master Mole-Cricket You did indeed, Father.

Father Mole-Cricket "And I wouldn't like to do that," I said, "dear me, no." Thank you very much for seeing us. It has been most interesting. But now, if you don't mind, we ought really to be getting along. You see, we are rather busy ourselves. There's the rice to plant and the chickens to feed and the ...

The two Mole-Crickets begin to bow themselves hurriedly from the Emperor's presence

Emperor Come here, Helmet!

He points to the ground at his feet and the Mole-Crickets scuttle back to the indicated position

If you succeed in the test you shall be rewarded.

Father Mole-Cricket Rewarded?

Chancellor It's the usual custom.

Emperor Complete the test and you shall be proclaimed Astrologer to the Court and you shall be granted my daughter's hand in marriage. What do you say to that?

Father Mole-Cricket It is not what I say, your Majesty, but what my wife will have to say, that will be more to the point.

Emperor Your wife!

Father Mole-Cricket Indeed yes, Majesty.

Emperor You have a wife already?

Father Mole-Cricket Alas, yes, Majesty.

Emperor This is ridiculous! It's all your fault, Chancellor. This was all your idea! The hand of the Princess in marriage—usual custom—common practice! Really, Chancellor! You'll have to do better than this! I shall lose my temper! I know I shall! It's going, Chancellor ... I can feel it going ...

Chancellor Majesty, Majesty, calm yourself! There is another solution!

Emperor Out with it, man! Out with it.

Chancellor Perhaps the assistant astrologer is unmarried?

Emperor Capital, Chancellor! (*To Master Mole-Cricket*) Are you unmarried?

Master Mole-Cricket Yes, Majesty.

Emperor Completely unengaged?

Master Mole-Cricket Indeed I am, Majesty.

Emperor No attachments or entanglements whatsoever?

Master Mole-Cricket Not one, Majesty.

Emperor Perfect! Succeed in the test and you shall win the hand of my daughter. What do you say to that?

Master Mole-Cricket yawns and glances across at the Princess. He is far too tired to contemplate matrimony

Master Mole-Cricket If it's all the same to you, Majesty, I should like to sleep on the suggestion. (*He yawns again*)

The Princess fumes inwardly

Emperor Sleep on it! I offer you the hand of a very presentable princess (although I say so myself), and you say you wish to sleep on it! A little wife to cook and sew, stitch and seam, bake and brew.

Master Mole-Cricket (*brightening*) Can she do all those things?

Emperor Of course not. She's a princess, isn't she? You can't have everything. But she can learn—while you're out earning her living.

Master Mole-Cricket Do you mean that I have to keep her as well?

The Princess is boiling with rage

Chancellor It's the usual custom.

Emperor Don't interrupt! Of course you will have to keep her.

Master Mole-Cricket Then I'd rather not if it's all the same to you.

Emperor It is not all the same to me! If I say you'll marry the girl—you'll marry the girl and like it. Now listen to me. Here is the test you must perform. Four thieves broke into the Royal Palace Vaults yesterday and stole four chests of my Royal Gold. It's your task, Frisket, to discover where those chests are hidden. Do you understand the test?

Father Mole-Cricket Only too well, Majesty.

Emperor Then get on with it, man! Goodness me, you can't expect the Royal Executioner to hang about waiting for you all day!

Father Mole-Cricket But, Majesty, it will be necessary for me to have time in which to perform such a task. We must have time, mustn't we, my boy?

Master Mole-Cricket Indeed, we must, Father.

Father Mole-Cricket You see, I must examine the stars and the skies and . . . and everything . . . through my telescope.

Emperor Your whichascope?

Chancellor I believe the instrument is called a whatascope, Majesty.

Emperor A howoscope?

Father Mole-Cricket A telescope. (*He proffers the telescope for the Emperor's inspection*) This is it. It's a very valuable telescope, Majesty. You might not believe it, but this telescope belonged to my late great-uncle, the Admiral of the Fleet. Perhaps you would care to read the inscription.

Look, it says, "Presented to Admiral Mole-Cricket on the occasion
of ..."
Emperor (*knocking the telescope aside*) I have no wish to see your grand-
mother's periscope, Hatchet!
Chancellor Whichascope.
Master Mole-Cricket Telescope.
Emperor Whatever it is, I don't want to see it! Now, just you see here,
Brisket, I've given you a task to do and you get on with it. Instead of
standing there nattering about your nephews and nieces and bioscopes! I
am not interested in your relations, Watchitt! I am interested in my four
chests of gold. Kindly locate them, Hoskitt! I can give you two minutes.
Father Mole-Cricket Two minutes! But, Majesty——
Emperor Two minutes, Docket. Two minutes. Or else ...

*Father Mole-Cricket points the telescope towards the ceiling and peers
through the eye-piece. Master Mole-Cricket yawns loudly. The Princess—who
is now in a turmoil of rage—can contain herself no longer*

Princess Young man, it is very rude to yawn in company.
Emperor Chancellor! She spoke! She said words!
Master Mole-Cricket (*completing his yawn*) I beg your pardon?
Princess I said it is extremely ill-mannered to snore.
Emperor Again! She spoke to him again!
Master Mole-Cricket (*to the Princess*) I don't see that it is any business of
yours.
Emperor He replies! Love, Chancellor—love, if ever I saw it!
Princess You are nothing but an ignorant, coarse, common and extremely
ill-bred boy.
Master Mole-Cricket I could say exactly the same things about you.
Except, of course, that you are a girl.
Emperor Wonderful, wonderful! They might be married a year already!
Princess In fact, it is quite beneath my dignity to hold a conversation with
you.
Master Mole-Cricket It is certainly beneath mine to speak to you.
Princess I have nothing further to say.
Master Mole-Cricket Nor I.

The Princess and Master Mole-Cricket turn their backs on each other

Emperor Chancellor, they are having their first quarrel! They were
obviously made for each other. If only her mother could have lived to see
this day! The marriage will take place immediately.
Chancellor If I might point out to your Majesty, there is still the test to be
completed.
Emperor Test? Test? What test?
Chancellor The missing chests of gold. They are still to be recovered.
Should these astrologers fail we have no other applicants to locate the
stolen chests.

Emperor Or marry the Princess.

Chancellor Or marry the Princess, Majesty. But if your Royal Majesty were to exercise your generosity and grant the astrologers the time they require—perhaps, Majesty, they may find the chests.

Emperor And the Princess will be married off at last, Chancellor!

Chancellor It is not beyond the bounds of possibility.

Emperor You know, Chancellor, I've just had an idea.

Chancellor Majesty?

Emperor How would it be if I were to give this astrologer time to find the chests? After all, Chancellor, if we execute this one—nobody remains to carry out the task, or marry the Princess.

Chancellor Your Majesty thinks of everything.

Emperor (*crossing to the Mole-Crickets*) Listen to me, Satchet!

Father Mole-Cricket lowers the telescope

I've decided to grant you your request. You shall have the time you ask for.

Father Mole-Cricket Thank you, Majesty, it's most——

Emperor I shall give you four days, Ticket, in which to study the stars through your ... your ...

Father Mole-Cricket Telescope?

Emperor Exactly. To study the stars, examine the skies, and return the four chests of gold.

Father Mole-Cricket You wouldn't care to extend the ...

Emperor Four days. That gives you a day for each chest. If you succeed, you shall be granted anything you wish to name. If you fail ... If you fail ... But there, there, we don't need to go into those morbid details now, do we?

Father Mole-Cricket I promise your Majesty that we will spend every single minute in studying the stars, and ... and searching the skies, and ... and ...

Master Mole-Cricket Looking through the telescope, Father?

Father Mole-Cricket Thank you, my boy. And looking through the telescope. I only hope, Majesty, that we may be able to repay your kindness by returning the four chests of gold.

Emperor And marrying the Princess?

Master Mole-Cricket Certainly not!

Princess The very idea!

Emperor Well—we'll see, we'll see. In the meantime, you may consider yourselves Acting Unpaid Astrologer and Assistant Astrologer at the Court of Indera Maya. That's all. You may go.

The two Mole-Crickets bow themselves out

Only remember, Locket! Four days! Four days—or else ...

Princess Father, I shall never so much as speak to that boy again as long as I live.

The Princess flounces out

Emperor You see, Chancellor—she adores the lad. Well, there we are. Now, be a good fellow and help me off with my robes. I do hate all this ceremony.

The Chancellor assists the Emperor to remove his robes and crown

Chancellor If I might be permitted to compliment your Majesty on the admirable way in which you have conducted the afternoon's proceedings, I should be very happy to do so.

Emperor You may, Chancellor, you may.

The Chancellor crosses and places the crown on the throne and the robes across the back of the throne

What was it I gave the Astrologer? Four days, did I say?

Chancellor You did indeed, Majesty.

Emperor Four days, eh? ... Tuesday, and so the fourth day will fall on Friday.

Chancellor Your Majesty is a mathematical genius.

Emperor Thank you, Chancellor. And we must both of us hope that nothing else should chance to fall on Friday. (*He gives the Chancellor a sly dig in the ribs*) Such as—heads for instance, eh? ...

Chancellor (*fingering his neck unhappily*) If your Majesty has no further need of me this afternoon ...

Emperor No. Nothing further.

The Chancellor bows himself across the room

Chin up, man! Chest out! And remember, Chancellor! Always expect the best—but be prepared for the worst.

Chancellor How true, Majesty. How very, very true!

The Chancellor exits L

Emperor What a pleasant fellow! How well he puts words together! ... (*He backs, thoughtfully, towards his throne and regally seats himself. As, however, he has unwittingly sat upon the points of his crown he rises quickly and unregally*) Chancellor! ... Chancellor!! ...

The Emperor is losing his temper as——

—the CURTAIN *falls*

ACT II

SCENE 1

Before the CURTAIN *rises the Chancellor enters and gazes dreamily into the middle distance for quite some time. He sighs ecstatically and then realizes that he has an audience*

Chancellor Oh! You're still here! Please forgive me—I had quite forgotten you. As a matter of fact, my mind was on other things. We are all human. Even my old heart is not too ancient to recognize a severe attack of love. But then, you saw it for yourselves—that boy, that girl—and I'm sure you've drawn your own conclusions. Is there one single one of you who didn't realize the moment that couple set eyes upon each other they were meant to fall in love? It's obvious the pair of them were fated for marriage from the instant this entertainment began. It isn't my fault that events have taken this turn, and you may have my word on that. In the play that was intended for this evening I was to marry the princess, and what a romance you would have seen then. I had the costume made especially for the part. It fits me perfectly. I should have carried that girl off in such a manner that would have won applause from every corner of this theatre. There would not have been a dry handkerchief in the house. That was what should have happened. What's a play compared with love? And to think that it was I that was instrumental in bringing them together! My old heart thumps at the thought. It's very romantic. What was it she called him? . . . Coarse, common, ill-bred—but what are words? I tell you, there was a look in that girl's eyes the like of which I've never seen before—except, of course, in the eyes of that boy. I may be an old fool, but from here on the play may progress as it will—I'll not impede it. I shall retire to a hiding place and watch what happens. (*He listens attentively for a moment, his ear to the curtain, then raises a finger to his lips*) Ssshhh! They are about to continue. I shall creep quietly away . . .

The Chancellor tiptoes off stage

The Curtain rises on the Mole-Cricket back garden. It is four days later. We discover Father Mole-Cricket sitting dejectedly in the garden and Master Mole-Cricket leaning against the veranda. Mother Mole-Cricket is sweeping the veranda with a broom. She pauses in her task to lean over the veranda and address her husband

Mother Mole-Cricket Well, all I can say is that it serves you right. It's no good coming to me for sympathy, you've brought all this upon yourself! (*She makes a further brisk sweep with the broom before leaning it against* *the door and crossing down into the garden*) If you had taken the trouble to listen to me in the first place, you wouldn't be in this position now. It's all this messing about with astrology and telescopes and things that don't concern you.

Father Mole-Cricket groans and turns away

But this much I will tell you: if you bring shame on this house by being publicly executed I shall never speak to you again. Royal Acting Unpaid Astrologer indeed! Such nonsense!

Father Mole-Cricket (*rising*) How was I to know that all this would happen?

Mother Mole-Cricket I said from the very beginning that no good would come of it. After all, if you decide to take all this interest in what goes on in the heavens, you can't start complaining when you're given the opportunity of a closer look. If you should chance to travel in that direction.

Father Mole-Cricket groans again

Master Mole-Cricket (*crossing down*) I wonder what time they'll come to take you away, Father?

Father Mole-Cricket I wish you'd both stop talking about it. It's bad enough as it is, without the pair of you going on and on and on ...

Master Mole-Cricket I expect they'll do it at dawn tomorrow. It usually happens at dawn. Dawn! What a terrible time to have to get out of bed!

Father Mole-Cricket It would serve you right if they chopped off your head as well. Don't forget, you are my assistant, you know.

Master Mole-Cricket You don't think they will, do you, Father?

Father Mole-Cricket I don't see why not.

Mother Mole-Cricket It's no more or less than either of you deserve. I only hope it teaches you both a lesson.

Master Mole-Cricket I shouldn't think they will bother with me, really. The Emperor will probably be quite satisfied with your head, Father.

Father Mole-Cricket groans again

Never mind. Cheer up. I have heard that you can have just what you like for breakfast on the last morning.

Father Mole-Cricket I don't suppose I shall feel like eating.

Master Mole-Cricket I'll come along with you, if you like, and give you a hand with what's left over.

Mother Mole-Cricket You'll do nothing of the kind. (*She returns to the veranda*) You'll bring it straight back here for the chickens.

Father Mole-Cricket You might, at least, wait until I'm dead before you start sharing out my breakfast.

Mother Mole-Cricket It's all very well for you, you'll have nothing to worry about, but it's no easy life being a widow these days. After all, you don't want to leave this world with the thought that you've left a starving wife and child behind.

Father Mole-Cricket I don't want to leave this world under any circumstances. I wish you'd leave me alone. I want to think.
Mother Mole-Cricket If you want my advice, the best thing you can do is
get some work done to take your mind off things. There is the wood to be
chopped.
Father Mole-Cricket And stop talking about chopping!
Mother Mole-Cricket Well, if all you're going to do is sit and sulk in the
garden, I, for one, have no time to stand and watch you. I've plenty of
things on my mind without troubling myself with your worries.

Mother Mole-Cricket flounces off into the house

Master Mole-Cricket She's quite right, you know, Father. It's not a bit of
use worrying about it now. (*He yawns*) We might just as well wait and let
things happen of their own accord ... And while we are waiting—we
might just as well be resting. (*He lies down on the grass*) I ... I do feel
rather sleepy ... It's all this fuss and bother, I think ... (*He is fast asleep*)
Father Mole-Cricket A fine family I've got! Resting indeed! As if I could
possibly rest with the thought of all this in my head. (*He feels his head
gingerly*) By this time tomorrow I won't have a head. (*He crosses and sits
on the veranda steps*) Who would have thought that four days could have
flown so quickly? Four days! As if I could possibly have found four
thieves in four days! And it's Friday already ... Four days. One—two—
three—four. Tuesday—Wednesday—Thursday—Friday. One—two—
three—four. As for the thieves, they're probably miles alway by now. One
thing's certain, at least—they certainly aren't likely to come anywhere
near this village ...

*As he speaks the four Thieves creep on R, in a sinister manner. The leader of
the thieves looks all around and then motions his men to follow him across
the garden*

Four days! What chance have I had? One ...

The Leader of the Thieves trots across the garden

Two ...

The First Thief trots across the garden

Three ...

The Second Thief trots across the garden

Four ...

The Third Thief trots across the garden

One-two-three-four ...

There is general consternation among the Thieves

First Thief Here! I can hear someone counting us!
Second Thief So can I!
Third Thief Me too!

Leader Will you be quiet! (*He peers around the garden and sees the sign*)
Mercy on us! Why this is the house of Father Mole-Cricket, the
astrologer! We are discovered!
First Thief Finished!
Third Thief That must be him over there!
Second Thief Listen! He's speaking again!
Leader Hush!
Father Mole-Cricket I know just what's going to happen. The Emperor is
going to expect me to say, (*loudly*) "I know who the thieves are, your
Majesty. I know their names. I know all about them, I can arrest them
whenever I like."

There is consternation among the Thieves

First Thief Indera Maya will have us hung!
Second Thief Hanged. And drawn!
Third Thief And quartered!
Leader Indera Maya will certainly have us hung . . .
Second Thief Hanged.
Leader I'm sorry. Hanged—and drawn and quartered.
Third Thief He might have pity on me. I only took the smallest chest.
First Thief That was because you couldn't carry a larger one. You're just as
bad as the rest of us.
Third Thief I'm not then!
First Thief You are then!
Third Thief Not then!
First Thief Are then!
Leader Be quiet both of you! We are all as bad as one another. Neither
more nor less than downright criminals. There is only one thing we can
do. We must give ourselves up.
First Thief Oh, no! If we give ourselves up we shall be whipped!
Second Thief If we give ourselves up we shall be beaten!
Third Thief If we give ourselves up we shall be flogged!
Leader If you don't do as I say, I shall whip and beat and flog you all
myself.
First Thief I vote we give ourselves up.
Second Thief Hear, hear!
Leader Good. Then we are all agreed. Come along, we must give ourselves
up to Father Mole-Cricket.

The four Thieves approach the veranda

Good-morning, Father Mole-Cricket!

*Father Mole-Cricket looks up. Master Mole-Cricket wakes, yawns, stretches
himself and rises*

Father Mole-Cricket Good-morning, gentlemen. Did you wish to see me?
Leader We have come to give ourselves up.
Father Mole-Cricket To what?
Leader To give ourselves up.

Father Mole-Cricket You'd better find a Royal Policeman, I'm far too busy at the moment.

Leader But we want to give ourselves up to you, Father Mole-Cricket.

First Thief And we promise we will never do it again.

Second Thief Never as long as we live.

Third Thief I only took the smallest chest, Father Mole-Cricket. It was so small I was sure that his Majesty would never notice it was missing.

The Leader of the Thieves pushes the Third Thief aside, impatiently

Father Mole-Cricket (*rising*): Excuse me, did you say 'chest'?

Third Thief *Smallest* chest, Father Mole-Cricket. The very smallest chest there was. I wouldn't have taken it otherwise.

Leader (*again brushing the Third Thief aside*) Will you be quiet! We should have known that you would have discovered us, Father Mole-Cricket.

Father Mole-Cricket (*crossing down into garden*) Oh yes! You should have known that. Did you hear that my boy! 'Chests', they said!

Master Mole-Cricket I did indeed, Father.

Leader If we had given the matter our careful consideration, Father Mole-Cricket, we would never have, er . . . borrowed the chests.

Father Mole-Cricket No, I'm sure you wouldn't. Four chests, wasn't it?

Leader That's right.

Third Thief Three large chests, Father Mole-Cricket, and one very small one. You will remember that I did mention that the small one was the one I took.

Leader (*again pushing the Third Thief aside*) Four chests, Father Mole-Cricket.

Father Mole-Cricket Well, well, well! Four chests, eh? Did you hear that, my boy?

Master Mole-Cricket Indeed I did, Father.

Father Mole-Cricket From his Majesty's Royal Vaults, would it be?

Leader Yes, yes. That's right. And now we have come to give ourselves up.

Father Mole-Cricket Have you now? You know, that was a very wise thing to do. Very wise.

Leader What will become of us, Father Mole-Cricket?

First Thief Will we be hung?

Second Thief Hanged. And drawn?

Third Thief And quartered?

Father Mole-Cricket Every bit of it, I should imagine. And a great deal more than that, I shouldn't wonder.

Leader Isn't there anything we can do?

Father Mole-Cricket Well . . . Yes, possibly there is. But first, you must do two things for me.

Second Thief We shall be only too pleased, Father Mole-Cricket, to help you in any way we can.

Leader No matter how great or small, we are yours to command.

Father Mole-Cricket Then first, you must promise that you won't be caught stealing again.

Leader We shall never be *caught* stealing again, Father Mole-Cricket.

First Thief We wouldn't think of it, Father Mole-Cricket.

Second Thief We wouldn't even consider any such similar malpractice.

Third Thief Not even the tiniest chest you could ever imagine. Even smaller than the one I took, that was very, very small indeed.

Leader The errors of all our past misdeeds lie heavy on all our unhappy hearts.

Father Mole-Cricket Good. And, secondly, you must tell me what you have done with the four chests of gold.

Leader You'll let us go free?

First Thief And we won't be hung—hanged?

Second Thief Or drawn?

Third Thief Not even quartered?

Father Mole-Cricket Not if you tell me what I want to know. I could, of course, easily look it up in the stars, you know. But if you care to confess it will save me the trouble of finding my spectacles. And you shall go free. But if I ever do study the stars and discover that you've been thieving again, I shall have no mercy whatsoever.

Leader I call for a general conference!

The four Thieves huddle together for a brief muttered conference. As they reach an agreement the Leader of the Thieves crosses to Father Mole-Cricket

We agree.

Father Mole-Cricket And the chests?

Leader We lost them, Father Mole-Cricket.

Father Mole-Cricket Lost them!

First Thief In a way.

Second Thief More or less.

Third Thief Generally speaking.

Leader Only this morning.

Second Thief Not more than an hour ago.

First Thief If that.

Third Thief Probably less.

Father Mole-Cricket Lost them!

Leader This is the way it was: you see, we chanced to call at an inn.

First Thief Not far from here.

Second Thief Just down the road.

Third Thief That's just what we did.

Leader And while we were there we met some sailors.

First Thief Very friendly they were.

Second Thief Or so we thought.

Third Thief That's how it seemed.

Leader Giving us drinks.

First Thief Plenty of money.

Second Thief Pockets were bulging.

Third Thief Oh, very nice men.

Leader What else could we think?

Father Mole-Cricket Go on . . .

Leader We were wrong. Rogues, they were, every one of them.

First Thief Robbers.

Second Thief Tricksters.

Third Thief Thieves.

Leader People like them deserve to be locked up.

Father Mole-Cricket What happened?

Leader One of them, the Captain I took him to be, by the way the others was a-speaking, suggests we play a game of cards. Well, like, it seems a harmless suggestion. A game of cards. As good a way to pass the time as any—us being sort of unemployed for the morning. Mostly we work nights, you see. So—off we goes. Believe it or not, Father Mole-Cricket, within the hour we'd lost every penny we possessed. Gambling, you know. It's been the downfall of many a respectable criminal.

Father Mole-Cricket You lost the gold?

Leader Every single piece.

Third Thief Even the smallest chest, Father Mole-Cricket, which you may recall I . . .

He is pushed aside by the leader of the Thieves

Father Mole-Cricket And the sailors? Are they still at this inn?

Leader (*shaking his head sadly*) No, no. That's the unhappy ending, as you might say. They upped and off with the chests of gold leaving us to pay for the drinks.

First Thief We had to pick the landlord's pocket.

Leader Said they had a tide to catch. A likely story.

Father Mole-Cricket You didn't by any chance, overhear the name of their ship?

Leader No, no. Unhappily not. But wait—I did get this. (*He takes a gold watch and chain from his pocket*) Whilst in the process of bending down to fasten my shoe-lace, my hand, inadvertently, strayed past the captain's jacket. Somehow or other, my fingers seemed to get caught up in the chain. I can't think how it happened. Imagine my surprise when, not two minutes ago, I found the article still to be in my possession. His watch, I think. (*He passes the watch to Father Mole-Cricket*) Gold all through. Eighteen carat. There's an inscription inside.

Father Mole-Cricket (*opening and reading the watch-case*) "Captain Bean-feast, Master of the *Bold Tassel*!"

Leader I suppose that might be the name you're seeking. There's also a motto in smaller writing. "Honesty is the best policy." What a lovely thought!

Father Mole-Cricket absent-mindedly closes the watch and is putting it in his pocket

Thanks very much.

Father Mole-Cricket (*returning the watch*) I beg your pardon.

The three thieves make a concerted grab for the watch but the Leader brushes them aside

Leader I quite understand. (*He returns the watch to his pocket*) Well, if that's all the information you require, Father Mole-Cricket you did say ...

Father Mole-Cricket Yes, that's all. Now, just you listen to me. I've decided to be lenient with you—this time. But whether the Emperor would feel the same way I wouldn't care to say. And so, if I were you, I should get out of here as quickly as you can and start running, and I shouldn't stop running until I came to ...

The four Thieves have already taken his advice and exited

Goodness me! They've gone!

Master Mole-Cricket What are you going to do now, Father?

Father Mole-Cricket *We*, my boy, are going to run away to sea.

Master Mole-Cricket But it's far too warm to run anywhere this morning!

Father Mole-Cricket It's our only chance. We must get down to the harbour ourselves, and climb aboard as quickly as we can. We must return with those four chests of gold, my son.

Master Mole-Cricket That's all very well, Father. But I still don't see why I have to go with you. I am feeling rather tired this morning and ...

Father Mole-Cricket You don't have to go with me, my boy. But remember, if the Emperor calls to chop off my head and my head isn't here to be chopped, he may very well lose his temper. He may even decide to chop off someone else's head instead. Yours, for instance. After all—you are the Assistant Acting Unpaid Royal Astrologer.

Master Mole-Cricket Now I see why I have to go with you.

Father Mole-Cricket Besides, when you say that you are going to run away to sea, it doesn't mean that you are going to run anywhere. It's merely a figure of speech.

Master Mole-Cricket Then what does it mean?

Father Mole-Cricket Simply, that you go down to the harbour and stow-away.

Master Mole-Cricket Stowaway?

Father Mole-Cricket Which means that you find a nice comfortable place to hide on board a ship. And then you go to sleep until someone comes along and finds you.

Master Mole-Cricket Nice comfortable place? Go to sleep? I think that running away to sea sounds like one of the best ideas you ever had! But we'd better do it quickly ... because ... (*he yawns*) because, I'm beginning to feel very ... very ... sleepy ...

Father Mole-Cricket Of course, there is your mother to consider. We'd better tell her ... No, wait! Perhaps we'd better not. She'd be sure to find some work for us to do before we went. I have it! We'll leave her a note ... (*He fumbles through his pockets and takes out a pencil and paper*) You bring me my telescope, my boy, we may need it.

Master Mole-Cricket collects the telescope from the veranda as his father writes the note

Dear wife ... We have found the Emperor's chests of gold. We must go to sea at once. .... There!

Master Mole-Cricket hands the telescope to his father

Thank you, son. And now, where can we leave this? . . . The very place!
(*He crosses to the sign and sticks the note on a jutting nail*) Your mother is
sure to see it there. And now! Ready, my boy?
Master Mole-Cricket I'm ready, Father.
Father Mole-Cricket Then off we go! (*He points, off, with the telescope*) To
sea! Come along, my boy! We must hurry!
Master Mole-Cricket (*yawning*) Coming, Father. . . . I'm coming!

Father Mole-Cricket exits L

Master Mole-Cricket yawns, stretches and trudges off L

A short pause before the Emperor enters R

Emperor Come along, Chancellor! Come along, man!

A weary Chancellor enters R

Chancellor Coming, Majesty . . . I'm coming . . .
Emperor Goodness me, Chancellor! One of these days you'll be late for
your own execution.
Chancellor (*sighing and sitting on the grass*) If I may be allowed to rest a
moment, Majesty. . . .
Emperor Rest? Rest! We can't rest now, Chancellor! We have business to
attend to. This man Cratchitt.
Chancellor The name is Cricket, Majesty. Mole-Cricket.
Emperor Never mind what the name is, Chancellor. Where is he? Why isn't
he here? He knows perfectly well that he has to be executed. The four days
are over, aren't they?
Chancellor They are indeed, Majesty.
Emperor Well then, why isn't he here? The executioner will be arriving from
the Palace at any minute with his wicket and we've no Hatchet—hatchet
and we've no Wicket.
Chancellor Cricket, Majesty.
Emperor Same game. Where is he? This is his house, isn't it?
Chancellor Indeed it is, Majesty. His name is on the board over there.
Emperor (*crossing to sign*) Board? . . . Board? . . . (*He takes down the note*)
Why! Bless my soul! . . . Chancellor, listen to this! "Dear wife. We have
found the Emperor's chests of gold. We must go to sea at once!"
Chancellor, he's gone to sea!
Chancellor (*still examining his aching feet*) To see what, Majesty?
Emperor To sea in a ship, you nincompoop! He's stolen my chests of gold
and gone to sea! Him and that son of his. To think that that boy was to
marry my daughter! A common thief. Just wait until I get my hands on
them. The fleet, Chancellor! That's the answer. We'll put to sea in the
Royal Fleet—bring them back—and then, Chancellor, and then . . . (*He
draws his finger across his throat*) On your feet, man! Up! Up! Chin in,
chest out! We must get down to the harbour at once.

The Chancellor climbs unhappily to his feet

Wait a minute! Take a message! Pencil! Paper!

The Chancellor takes his notebook and pencil from his robes

We must leave a note for the Royal Executioner. Ready?

The Chancellor inclines his head

Then put this: "Bring the axe to the harbour. We'll do it there." Got that?
Good.

*The Chancellor tears out the page and hands it to the Emperor who fixes it on
the nail on the sign*

There! Now, Chancellor! To the harbour! Quick march! To the sea! Joy,
joy, joy! I do love ships!

The Emperor hurries off L

The Chancellor moves as if to follow him, hesitates and addresses the audience

Chancellor One of these days I'm going to tell that man exactly what I think
of him. Emperor or no Emperor. And it won't be very pleasant. I don't
mind telling you. All right, let him chop off my head. At least I'll have had
the satisfaction of knowing that I've told him the truth, for once.
"Emperor," I shall say, "Emperor, I have only one thing to say to you,
and it's this . . ."
Emperor (*off*) Chancellor! . . . Chancellor!!
Chancellor Coming, Majesty! I'm coming.

*He turns to the audience as if to speak again, changes his mind, sighs and
limps off* L

*The door at the rear opens and Mother Mole-Cricket enters. She carries a
bundle of firewood and a small hatchet*

Mother Mole-Cricket (*calling from the veranda*) Husband! Idler! Good-for-
nothing! Come here at once and chop this wood! (*She crosses down into
the garden and looks around*) It's no use hiding! The work must be done!
(*She sees the note on the sign, glances down at the hatchet*) "Bring the axe
to the harbour. We'll do it there." We'll do nothing of the kind! (*She puts
the bundle of wood on the ground and sits on it*) We'll do it right here—or
not at all!

She is patiently waiting for her missing husband as——

—*the* CURTAIN *falls*

SCENE 2

The deck of the Bold Tassel—*at sea. Later the same day*

*The deck of this disreputable pirate ship has a general air of untidiness:
tangled ropes and rigging etc. There is a hatchway on the right, leading to*

*cabins, hold etc. A ship's locker is at the rear, on either side of which is a small
cannon with muzzle pointing through the deck-rail and out to sea. There is an
untidy heap of sailcloth, left, beneath which are hidden the two Mole-Crickets,
though we cannot see them. The four chests of gold are stacked beside the
sailcloth. Above the hatch is the bridge with a companionway to the deck. The
Captain and Mate stand on the bridge. The Mate is steering the ship by means
of a long tiller-shaft, while the Captain examines the horizon through his
telescope. The first sailor, Henry, is sitting on the ship's locker haphazardly
coiling a length of rope. His comrade, the second sailor Fred, is leaning against
the deck-rail and staring out to sea*

Captain (*closing the telescope*) What's your course, Mr Mate?
Mate Nor' by Nor' West, sir!
Captain Hold her steady as you go!
Mate Steady it is, Captain!

*The Captain crosses down the companionway to the deck and addresses
Henry, who is getting himself hopelessly entangled in the rope*

Captain Belay there, you bow-legged son of a sea-cook! Blister my barna-
cles! Frightening figureheads, sailorman! What do you think you're
playing at?
Henry (*vainly attempting to extricate himself from the rope*) Stowing away
the ropes and rigging, Captain!
Captain Suffering sea-chests, hearty! Three hours out from port and my
fore-peak looks like a mangled messdeck! Get this craft cleaned up
shipshape, seamanlike, smartish, or by the Penzance Pirates I'll have you
in irons!
Henry (*finally freeing himself and saluting*) Aye, aye, Captain!
Captain And stow those chests in the forward hold. Lumbering landlub-
bers, seaman, shall we advertise the Emperor's gold to every flyblown
frigate we chance to pass on course!
Henry Aye-aye, Captain!

The Captain exits through the hatchway

*Henry moves to carry out his orders. He struggles to lift the first chest but is
unsuccessful. His eye falls on Fred, who has taken a brown paper bag from his
pocket and is unconcernedly tossing bread crumbs over the side of the ship.
From here on can be heard the steady sound of snoring from beneath the
sailcloth*

Henry Fred! ... Fred!
Fred What is it now, Henry?
Henry Would you be so good as to tell me just what you think you're
doing?
Fred I'm only feeding the seagulls, Henry.
Henry Feeding the seagulls!
Fred Why? Have I done something wrong?
Henry Feeding the seagulls! A fine sort of sailor you've turned out to be!

Fred Why? What's the matter now?

Henry Oh . . . never mind. For goodness sake, look slippy and show a leg and help me to get these chests stowed away. The Captain's going crazy and all you can do is feed the seagulls!

Fred (*returning the paper bag to his pocket and crossing to join Henry*) Have we got to take them downstairs, Henry?

Henry Downstairs? Downstairs! Below, Fred, below. Will you try and remember!

Fred Oh, have done, Henry. I'm sure I do my best.

Henry Well, I'm sorry. But sometimes it does seem as if you weren't cut out for this sort of life. Now, just you take hold of that end and I'll take this. When I count to three we'll lift. Ready?

They position themselves at either side of the first chest

Wait a minute.

They lower the chest and Henry listens carefully

I can hear something unseamanlike

Fred Aye! Now that you come to mention it—so can I.

Henry Fred, it sounds to me just like somone snoring.

Fred Aye! Now that you come to mention it—so it does. Two someones.

Henry Fred, that snoring we hear is coming from underneath that there sailcloth.

Fred Aye! Now that you come to mention it—so it is.

The two Sailors tiptoe across to the sailcloth

Henry I'd say, offhand like, that this is something that ought to be investigated and looked into. I'd say, in a manner of speaking, that you and me, Fred, ought to have a look.

Fred Quite right. It's our duty. Go on . . . you first.

Henry No! Now! Be fair!

Fred Both together then.

Henry Agreed. When I give the word. Ready? One . . . two . . . three . . .

The two Sailors drag back the sailcloth to reveal the two Mole-Crickets, who wake in surprise

Well I never!

Fred Neither did I!

Father Mole-Cricket Good-afternoon, gentlemen!

Master Mole-Cricket Hello.

Henry And what might you two think you're up to? No good, I'll be bound, whatever it is.

The Two Mole-Crickets rise unceremoniously and dust themselves down

Father Mole-Cricket Well, sir, you see, it's like this: we decided, that is my son and I decided, to run away to sea. Didn't we, my boy?

Master Mole-Cricket Indeed we did, Father.

Henry Run away to sea?

Father Mole-Cricket In short, my good friend, we decided to become stowaways, didn't we, my son?

Master Mole-Cricket That is exactly what we decided, Father.

Father Mole-Cricket And so, here we are.

Henry Stowaways!

Fred Stowaways!

Henry On our ship!

Father Mole-Cricket Yes. And that is just what we did. We crept aboard in the harbour, looked around, found this very comfortable pile of canvas and then we. . . . we fell asleep.

Master Mole-Cricket Nothing could have been easier.

Father Mole-Cricket And now, if you'll excuse us, we'd like to go back to sleep again and go on being stowaways . . .

Master Mole-Cricket That's the most important part of being a stowaway, going to sleep . . .

Father Mole-Cricket In a nice comfortable place. So if you'll just pretend that you haven't seen us we can get back under . . .

Henry But we can't have stowaways on board this ship. Can we Fred?

Fred It wouldn't do at all.

Father Mole-Cricket Wouldn't it?

Henry Why, it isn't right and proper. Is it, Fred?

Fred That it isn't.

Father Mole-Cricket Not even just this once?

Henry No, I'm sorry. We just can't have it. You see, we're pirates.

Father Mole-Cricket Pirates!

Fred That we are.

Henry Why, we've been pirating now, on and off, for years and years. Haven't we, Fred?

Fred As long as I can remember.

Henry Scourging the seven seas and what have you, terrorizing every port and all that kind of thing. What! I reckon we're about the wickedest pirates as ever set foot aboard ship. Barring none. Right, Fred?

Fred Right enough.

Henry No, we couldn't have stowaways on board. You'd better come along with us and see the Captain.

Master Mole-Cricket The Captain!

Henry He's a proper old piratical pirate and no mistake, is the Captain. Shouting and swearing and carrying on and that sort of thing. You'll like him. What he's going to have to say about this, I can't imagine.

Fred I don't dare to think.

Henry (*pushing the two Mole-Crickets towards the hatch*) Come on, then! Lively, now!

Father Mole-Cricket If it's all the same to you, we'd rather not, thank you very much. I don't think that stowing away was such a very good idea after all . . .

Master Mole-Cricket Indeed it wasn't, Father . . .

Father Mole-Cricket And it does seem a pity to have to disturb your Captain. I'm sure he must be very busy driving the ship and . . . and everything. So, if it's all the same to you, we could slip over the side and swim back home.

Henry I'n not so sure that . . .

Master Mole-Cricket It isn't very far to the shore and we wouldn't mind in the least.

Henry If that's what you both want to do, of course . . .

Father Mole-Cricket It is, it is!

Master Mole-Cricket Indeed it is.

Henry Oh . . . all right then. Off you go.

Father Mole-Cricket (*crossing to the deck rail and hoisting a leg over the side*) Thank you very much.

Henry 'Course, there is the sharks . . .

Father Mole-Cricket (*hastily withdrawing his leg*) Sharks?

Henry I shouldn't worry. There can't be all that many in these waters. Hundred or so . . . What would you say, Fred?

Fred Hundred at the very most.

Henry Quoting a round figure. I shouldn't worry. Off you go.

The two Mole-Crickets edge nervously away from the side of the ship

The Captain enters through the hatchway

Father Mole-Cricket A hundred?

Master Mole-Cricket Sharks?

Captain (*approaching*) Rattle my rigging! What's this!

Henry Begging your pardon, Captain. But me and my shipmate here uncovered these two stowaways.

Fred That's right.

Captain Trembling topsails! Stowaways on my ship!

Master Mole-Cricket We didn't mean to . . .

Captain Batten my hatches! I've never heard the like! Stowing away on a pirate ship! I've never come across the same in all my natural bad days at sea. It's unethical! Do you know what I do with stowaways?

Father Mole-Cricket No, sir.

Captain How would you like to walk my plank, eh?

Father Mole-Cricket Not very much.

Captain Or swing from my yard-arm?

Master Mole-Cricket No, thank you.

Captain Touch of the rope's end, say? Thirty or forty lashes? Or how about an hour's keel-hauling?

Father Mole-Cricket It's most generous of you to offer, but you see, we really intended to . . .

Captain (*the full horror of the situation dawning upon him*) Stowing away on a pirate ship! Muttering mizzen masts, if this gets around I shall be the laughing stock from Lisbon to Cadiz!

Fred And Fastnet and Cromarty.

Captain Speak when you're spoken to!

Father Mole-Cricket We didn't mean any harm, sir, Captain . . .

Master Mole-Cricket Indeed we didn't . . .

Captain Harm! Sink me off Portugal! Harm! How do you think I'm going
to feel if the other pirate captains hear of this! Have you ever been kidded
by Kidd? Has Morgan ever made a mockery of you? Harm, he says, the
blundering lubber! Thirty years, I've spent, thirty years and more of
scourging the seven seas—saying nothing of the oceans. Thirty years a-
piling up my piratical reputation. Feared I was. Feared in every harbour
town by every mother's son—aye, and dreaded by many a dark-eyed
daughter. And now this has to happen. Stowaways! On board my ship!
(*He is almost in tears at the thought. He pulls out a large red spotted
handkerchief and blows his nose lustily*) I . . . I shall never dare show my
prow in port again. Blow my binnacles, if I will . . .
Henry What shall we do with them, Captain?
Captain Do with them! I'll spread their bones across the ocean! Clattering
cutlasses, lads! I'll show them! Clap them in irons the pair of them.
Suffering sea-chests! I'll feed them both to the sharks before I'm through,
swamp me if I won't. (*In his anger he has been twisting his telescope in his
hands. It finally comes apart in two pieces*) Murdering mermaids! Now I've
broken my telescope!
Father Mole-Cricket You can borrow mine if you like. (*He offers the
Captain his telescope*)
Captain (*taking the telescope*) Thanks very much. (*He turns to the two
Sailors*) Blundering bulkheads! Don't just stand there, you swabs! Place
me a plank on the side of my ship! Move yourselves, men! Or, by my
cross-bones, I swear I'll splash the pair of you amongst the billows!
Henry Aye-aye, Captain!

*The two Sailors exit left to return with a long plank. They open a "gate" in
the deck-rail and the plank is thrust out to overhang the ocean*

Father Mole-Cricket But, sir, Captain . . . your Admiralship . . . it's all been
a terrible mistake. We had no idea you were pirates . . .
Master Mole-Cricket Indeed we hadn't . . .
Father Mole-Cricket (*crossing to Captain to plead his case*) You see, when
the Emperor lost his chests of gold he ordered me to . . .
Captain (*drawing his cutlass and forcing Father Mole-Cricket back*) What's
this, what's this! The Emperor's chests, is it? So that's your fancy! Hear
that, my hearties? This pair of prying noseyparkers were out to purloin
your dishonest earnings! What's their future now, my buckoes?
Henry Shove them to the sharks!
Fred Cast them adrift without a craft, Captain!
Henry Scuttle the pair of them!
Fred Overboard, Captain!
Captain Aye, lads, aye! By Blackbeard's ghost I'll lay, this afternoon, that
both of you shall grub for gold in Davy Jone's locker!
Father Mole-Cricket But, Captain, you don't understand . . .
Master Mole-Cricket Indeed you don't . . .
Father Mole-Cricket All we meant was . . .
Captain Nattering Neptune! Hold your tongues! Pestering poopdecks!
They'll drive me mad! Over the side with you! Say your goodbyes and get

on with it! You can't keep the sharks waiting! (*He prods Father Mole-Cricket on to the plank*)
Father Mole-Cricket Goodbye, my boy.
Master Mole-Cricket Goodbye, Father. I shall be right behind you.
Captain (*prodding Father Mole-Cricket along the plank*) And now you can paddle your feet in my ocean ...

Father Mole-Cricket is edging his way along the plank as the Mate crosses and calls from the bridge

Mate Captain! ... Captain!
Captain Galloping galleons! What is it now?
Mate Thirty or forty ships off our bows, sir!
Captain Scuttle my scuppers! What's this!
Mate With the wind in their sails and bearing down!
Captain Where away, Mr Mate?
Mate (*pointing out to sea*) Yonder, Captain!
Captain (*peering out to sea through the telescope*) Battling battleships! An oceanful of men-of-war. Lash your tiller, Mr Mate! I'll need your services on deck!
Mate Aye-aye, Captain.
Captain Lively, lads, and stand to arms! You there, cully! Get the prisoners below! We've no time now for entertainment!
Henry Aye-aye, Captain!

Henry draws a pistol from his belt and ushers the two Mole-Crickets across the deck and through the hatchway. As they enter he slams and bolts the door

Captain And you, my hearty! Break open my powder chest! Flay my fo'c'sle, hurry, man! By thunder, they shall taste the power of my cannon!
Fred Aye-aye, Captain!

Fred throws open the locker as Henry returns and the Mate hurries down from the bridge. The Captain again studies the approaching fleet

Captain Ambling anchors, lads! It's Indera Maya's navy with the flag-ship to the fore! We've been spotted!
Henry If Indera Maya's fleet sees us we'll be blown to little pieces!
Fred Or sunk to the bottom!
Mate Or swallowed by sharks!
Captain Blistering bilge-pumps, shipmates! Don't stand there burbling! Pass out the shot and give them a broadside! Stand to your cannon, hearties! The least we'll do is go down fighting!
Fred Aye-aye, Captain!

He hands the articles from the locker to Henry who places them by the side of the cannons

Two little bags of powder!
Henry One for you—one for me ...
Fred Two wooden ramrods ...

Henry One for you—one for me . . .

Fred Two long cotton fuses . . .

Henry One for you—one for me . . .

Captain Hurry, men, hurry!

Fred Two`shiny black cannon balls . . . (*He pauses, searches in the bottom of the locker, and then rises slowly with a guilty expression*)

Captain Suffering seagulls! What's the matter now!

Henry Come along, Fred! What are you waiting for . . . Oh, Fred! Don't tell me! You've been and gone and done it again. I can tell by your face.

Captain Done it! Done what?

Henry He's forgotten the cannon balls!

Captain Forgotten the cannon balls?

Henry You have, haven't you?

Fred hangs his head in shame and tries hard to suppress an inane smile

And you can just wipe that silly grin off your face. It's nothing to laugh at.

Fred I'm sorry, Henry.

Henry It's no good being sorry. That won't help matters. Who's going to swim back and fetch them, that's what I'd like to know?

Captain Forgotten the cannon balls!

Mate We shall surely be swallowed by sharks!

Captain Stave in my sides, shipmates! *We're done for!* (*He turns the telescope over in his hands*) Plundering pirates! Look at this!

Mate Come abroad, Captain? What's awash?

Captain The telescope! Open your portholes, lads, and listen to this. "Presented to Admiral Mole-Cricket on the occasion of his assuming command of the Emperor's Fleet"! Crumbling capstans, shipmates! We're holding the Admiral's telescope!

Henry Then those two we've put below must be . . .

He leaves the sentence unfinished as the Pirates stare fearfully at the locked hatch

Captain The Admiral of the Royal Fleet himself, or my name isn't Bertram Beanfeast! And the little one's his second in command, as like as not!

The two Sailors fall on their knees in fright

Henry The Admiral of all the Fleet!

Fred And his second in command!

Captain As like as not. And you sorry sons of sailormen was suggesting we throw them both over the side. Clustering crowsnests! What's to become of us now!

Henry Blown to little pieces!

Fred Sunk to the bottom!

Mate Swallowed by sharks!

Captain The game's up, lads. We've come to the end of all our oceans. We must . . . make fast, heave to, and stand by to drop anchor in our final port. (*He wipes away a tear*) Mr Mate!

Mate Aye-aye, Captain!

Captain Be so good as to request the Admiral to kindly step up on deck. I shall have to ... hand over my command.

Mate (*crossing to hatchway*) As you say, Captain.

Captain It's a sorry business, lads. But every pirate has to face his punishment someday.

Mate (*opening the hatch door*) Would you both be so good as to grace our humble deck-boards with your sea-going presences? Captain would consider it more than kind if you'd grant him the honour of passing a word or two.

The two Mole-Crickets stumble warily on deck

Captain Why, there you are! Lumbering life-boats, shipmates! What a joy it is to have you on board my unhappy craft.

Father Mole-Cricket Indeed, we're both very happy to be on board, Captain. And, if it's all the same to you, sir, we'd very much like to stay on board.

Master Mole-Cricket We would indeed.

Father Mole-Cricket You see, we don't really want to walk the plank. There are the sharks to consider and ...

Captain Plank? Sharks? Come, come now! Surely you're not suggesting ... I'll not believe it! You didn't take our little joke to be in earnest?

Father Mole-Cricket Joke?

Master Mole-Cricket You didn't mean it?

Captain (*forcing a laugh*) Just listen to that, my hearties! These two gentlemen took our little seamanlike playful pranks to heart! They thought we were serious!

Henry (*forcing a laugh*) Would you believe it!

Mate Did you ever hear the like!

Fred What a scream!

Captain Why! Surely you judged old Cap'n Beanfeast better than that! Or ... should I say: Beaming Bertram Beanfeast, as I'm known around the ports. Eh, Mr Mate?

Mate That you are, Captain. The life and soul of every port. The kindest heart, I've heard it said, in any harbour. Eh, men?

Henry The kiddies love him.

Fred A kind word and a pat on the head for them all.

Captain There are you! Planks indeed! That's a good one, that is! Now, now, sir! Come now! I'll not have that. Tell the truth. You saw through our little subterfuge the minute you set foot aboard. Just the same, you'll pardon me saying so, as we saw through yours.

Father Mole-Cricket Mine?

Captain That we did, you'll excuse me mentioning it. Why, the very minute I clapped my eyes on the pair of you, I says to myself, "Bertram," Bertram being the name my mother gave me. "Bertram, that there's no ordinary pair of stowaways," I says.

Father Mole-Cricket Did you really?

Captain And then, in a flash, there it was! "Why, Bertram Beanfeast," I
says, "if it isn't the Admiral of the Fleet himself! A-come aboard to take
command!"

Father Mole-Cricket Admiral?

Captain And his second in command. And then it was, you see, that little
bit of devilment in every simple sailor's heart took hold of me. Right, Mr
Mate?

Mate You always was the one for a laugh, Captain.

Henry Has us all in stitches.

Fred He'd have you split your sides, he would.

Captain No, no. You never had me fooled for a second. Long before I took
the liberty of reading your name, for myself, on your telescope. You can
have it back now. (*He proffers the telescope to Father Mole-Cricket*)

Father Mole-Cricket (*taking the telescope*) Thanks very much.

Captain Not at all. Thank you—Admiral.

Master Mole-Cricket Father. He means *your* name on the telescope!

Father Mole-Cricket So he does! So he does indeed! Goodness me! It was
very foolish of me, Captain, to lend you the telescope.

Captain Not at all, Admiral. What! Old Bertram had seen through your
disguise a long time ago, make no mistake about that. Being up to all the
harmless sea-going wheezes myself, so to speak.

Father Mole-Cricket Yes, yes. I can see that.

Captain Now all that remains for me to do is hand you my sword.

*The Captain draws his cutlass from his belt and passes it to Father Mole-
Cricket. The Pirates, in unison, take out their pistols and cutlasses and drop
them on the deck*

Admiral, my craft's yours to command.

Father Mole-Cricket There is one other thing . . .

Captain You'll be meaning the Emperor's chests of gold, I fancy. I was just
coming to that. No sooner said than mentioned. (*He indicates the chests*)
You can see for yourself, I've had them all prepared and ready to await
your Admiral's conveyance . . . If I might make so bold as to beg one final
consideration?

Father Mole-Cricket Yes?

Captain My ship, my men, my mate and myself have done our utmost,
during your short and deeply honoured visit, to . . . er . . . entertain your
Importances in, shall we say, our own simple seamanlike fashion.

Father Mole-Cricket Go on . . .

Captain I wonder . . . in return . . . Admiral, we're at your mercy.

Father Mole-Cricket You know, I do feel rather sorry for you all. And it is
possible, if you do exactly as I say, that I maybe able to put in a good
word for you, with my friend the Emperor.

Captain We'd be ever so grateful.

Henry And we won't be blown to little pieces?

Fred Or sunk to the bottom?

Mate Or swallowed by sharks?

Father Mole-Cricket Not if you do as I tell you.

Captain Broadside my beam-end, my hearties! I vote we do as he says!
Pirates Aye-aye, Captain.
Father Mole-Cricket But first you must promise to give up being pirates and you must never, ever again, scourge the seas or terrorize another port.
Captain Batten my hatches!
Father Mole-Cricket If you don't promise you know what will happen.
Henry Little pieces!
Fred The bottom!
Mate Sharks!
Captain I vote we promise.
Pirates Aye-aye, Captain.
Father Mole-Cricket Good. Quickly, then, there isn't much time and the Emperor's Fleet is almost upon us. First, you must turn the ship round and sail back to the harbour. And you two sailors must find some brushes and paint and rags and clean up the decks on the way.
Captain Is that all, Admiral?
Father Mole-Cricket I'll explain the rest of my plan when we dock. But this ship must be spick and span and seamanlike before we drop anchor—and we must be there before the Emperor.
Captain Leave it to me, Admiral! Capering cannons, lads! What are you waiting for? You heard the Admiral's orders! Run up that rigging and give me some sail!
Pirates Aye-aye, Captain.

The two Sailors climb the rigging as the Captain and the Mate return to the bridge

Master Mole-Cricket What now, Father? And how are we going to explain everything to his Majesty?
Father Mole-Cricket Leave all that to me, my boy. I have an idea. Just at the moment . . . I am feeling rather tired . . .
Master Mole-Cricket I'm feeling rather tired too, Father . . .
Father Mole-Cricket We might as well . . . (*He yawns*) We might just as well finish our sleep, my boy . . .

The two Mole-Crickets make themselves comfortable in the sail-cloth

Master Mole-Cricket Now that is a good idea, Father . . . A very good idea, indeed . . .
Captain (*leaning over the bridge*) Hoist your mains'l!
Pirates Aye-aye, Captain.
Captain Round your rudder! Broaden your tops'l! Find some pots and paint the poop-deck! And hurry it up, hearties! We're putting to port!
Pirates Aye-aye, Captain!

The Pirates are indulging in great activity, the Mole-Crickets are gently snoring as——

—*the* CURTAIN *falls*

SCENE 3

The deck of the Bold Tassel—*in harbour. Evening of the same day*

Before the CURTAIN *rises the Chancellor enters to address the audience*

Chancellor What a day! Tossed like a cockle-shell about the ocean and my
stomach is still going in and out with the tide. Even if we were ready to
begin the play—which we aren't—I should be quite incapable of giving
you a reasonable performance. If you wish to go on sitting out there like a
lot of stuffed dummies, do so by all means—it's your own time. I beg your
pardon. Please forgive me. The truth is, my stomach is not at all well.
Accept my apology. Please believe me, when the evening started I had
everything planned meticulously down to the last detail. No triviality was
overlooked. Oh, and the play I had arranged for you to see! Wonderful,
wonderful! I had arranged to play the hero. I was going to cut and thrust
and hack my way through more villains than have ever been gathered
together at one time before. And the dialogue! Perfect! Crisp, clean and
sharp as a pin. Snip, snap, snip. I tell you, the words would have crackled
like a bonfire. I wrote the script myself. All that work and now this. No
play and, confidentially, between ourselves, very nearly no players. The
way the Emperor is feeling at the moment I shouldn't be at all surprised if
there were very few heads left before this night is out. In fact, I shouldn't
be surprised if the Emperor were to start on you. This much I will tell
you—that so-called astrologer and his assistant will be the first to go. We
have them caught like traps in a rat—raps in a trat—trats in a . . . Oh,
what's the use! My nerves are on edge, my spirit is broken, my stomach is
queasy, my feet are almost dropping off, my head aches . . . My head!
Now why did I have to mention that word! Something must be done. And
urgently. With your permission we shall start all over again. From the
beginning. Curtain please!

The CURTAIN *begins to rise*

Our scene is set, you will remember, in the back garden of the house of
Father Mole-Cricket.

The CURTAIN *goes up on the ship-board set. The Chancellor throws up his
hands in disgust and addresses someone in the wings*

Can you never get anything right? Ever?

*The ship is now looking much tidier—ropes neatly coiled, deck clear of
sailcloth, etc. The four chests have been removed. The "gate" in the deck-rail
is open giving access to the gang-plank which runs on to the harbour wall. A
harbour backcloth has been lowered*

The Chancellor, in annoyance, is crossing to leave the ship

*Before he reaches the gang-plank, however, the Emperor and the Princess
come aboard. The Emperor is pulling the Princess by the hand—she is
suffering from a fit of "sulks"*

Emperor Look here, Chancellor! Be good enough to explain to me just what is going on!

Chancellor Going on, Majesty?

Emperor You know what I mean, Chancellor. Answer my question and kindly assist me by not beating about the hedge.

Chancellor Bush, Majesty.

Emperor Eh? What's that?

Chancellor Your Majesty suggested that I was beating about the bush. In short, Majesty, that I was hedging.

Emperor Isn't that what I said?

Chancellor I . . . I rather believe that it is, Majesty.

Emperor Well then, stop contradicting me, Chancellor! I know what I'm saying. After all, it's me that's saying it. You must learn to keep a still head in your tongue, my good fellow.

Chancellor Tongue in my head, Majesty.

Emperor Chancellor, one more word from you and you will have neither tongue nor head to put it in. Do I make myself clear?

Chancellor (*bowing low*) You do indeed, Majesty.

Emperor Good. Very good, Chancellor. As long as we understand each other. As for you, my girl, I'll put a stop to your stupidity. You weep when I find you a likeable lad and wail when I want to get rid of him. I'll marry you off to a one-legged sailor and you shall spill your tears in the ocean.

He releases the Princess who crosses to continue her sulking by the deck-rail

Princesses, Chancellor, are ten times as troublesome as twenty ordinary daughters.

The Chancellor bows low

And now, perhaps, we can get to the bottom of this affair. This is the ship we've been chasing up and down the ocean, isn't it?

Chancellor It is indeed, Majesty.

Emperor The ship, in fact, that those astrologers were on?

Chancellor The very same, Majesty.

Emperor And we are in my Royal Harbour, aren't we?

Chancellor We are indeed, Majesty.

Emperor Where my Royal Executioner was ordered to meet me, in fact?

Chancellor The exact same spot.

Emperor Then where is the Royal Executioner? Eh? Why isn't he here? And where's that fellow, Ticket?

Chancellor Ticket, Majesty?

Emperor That's what I said. The Acting Unpaid Royal Astrologer. What does he call himself? Cloakroom-Ticket?

Chancellor Mole-Cricket, Majesty.

Emperor (*ominously*) What did you say, Chancellor?

Chancellor I didn't speak, Majesty.

Emperor Good for you, Chancellor. And now, Chancellor, you will speak. You will tell me what has happened to my executioner, my chests of gold and that man Nugget. You will tell me now, Chancellor . . . or else!

Chancellor Or else . . . Majesty.

Emperor (*drawing his finger across his throat*) Or else, Chancellor . . .

Chancellor I rather fear, Majesty, that the present circumstances would appear to be beyond my control. It would seem that . . . Wait a minute! Here's someone coming aboard now!

Emperor Eh? What's that?

Mother Mole-Cricket, carrying the hatchet and firewood, marches up the gang-plank and on to the deck

Mother Mole-Cricket Where is he? Where is that lazy good-for-nothing husband of mine? Walked all the way, I have, with these! Bring them to the harbour, he said. Thinking, you see, I wouldn't come, he'd get out of doing it. He was wrong. Oh, yes! Here I am and here I'll stay and here he'll set about the job. Just wait till I lay my hands on him. Where is he, eh?

Chancellor Now look here, my good woman, do you realize that you are speaking to his Royal Majesty, Indera Maya?

Mother Mole-Cricket I don't care if I'm speaking to the Emperor himself! All I want to do is get within an arm's length of that idle, loafing, lounging layabout, I'll . . .

The hatch door opens and Father Mole-Cricket and Master Mole-Cricket enter

Father Mole-Cricket Did someone call my name?

Mother Mole-Cricket So there you are!

Emperor Wicket?

Chancellor Cricket!

Father Mole-Cricket Majesty! (*He bows low*)

Master Mole-Cricket Majesty! (*He bows low*)

Mother Mole-Cricket The Emperor! (*She bows low*)

Princess Him!

Master Mole-Cricket That dreadful girl again!

Emperor Now see here, Locket! You've caused quite enough trouble already! Hasn't he caused enough trouble, Chancellor?

Chancellor He has indeed, Majesty.

Emperor More than enough. Your head should have been off ages ago and here you are, as bold as brass, walking around as if you owned it yourself! The sooner we get it off your shoulders the better for all concerned. If you only knew the business we had to go into to arrange these things! Death certificates, burial certificates, executioner's authorizations, executioner's fees, chaplain's fees, grave-digger's fees. It all has to be cleared by the treasury, you know. The expense you're causing the general public is nobody's business. And the forms to fill in! Tell him about the forms, Chancellor.

Chancellor There's the import permit for the axe, Majesty, spectators applications to be granted, petitions for reprieve to be refused, there's the . . .

Emperor That's enough, Chancellor. Perhaps now, Nugget, you've got some idea of the nuisance you're causing. So now, if you'll say you're sorry, bend down, bare your neck, we can get the whole thing over and done with.

Father Mole-Cricket But, Majesty, if you'll only give me time to explain . . .

Emperor I've no wish to hear your excuses, Crockett. Explain indeed! Running off with my chests of gold! No, Tisket. Certainly not, Tasket! Now be a good chap, do as you're told and don't let us hear any more of this nonsense about excuses.

Father Mole-Cricket But, Majesty, we weren't running away with your chests of gold, were we, my son?

Master Mole-Cricket Indeed, we weren't, your Majesty.

Father Mole-Cricket We ran away to sea to recover the chests!

Master Mole-Cricket That's just what we did!

Emperor It's no good, Biscuit. I have not the slightest intention of paying the slightest attention.

Father Mole-Cricket And . . . and not only that, Majesty. But we also ran away to sea in order to collect your Majesty's present.

Emperor No, Digget! You won't get round me like that. You must be punished. Mustn't he be punished, Chancellor?

Chancellor Indeed he must, Majesty.

Emperor So it isn't a bit of use coming to me with your tales of presents and expecting that . . . Wait a minute! Did you say—present?

Father Mole-Cricket I did indeed, Majesty.

Emperor My present! You . . . You've brought me a present! I love getting presents! Where is it? What is it? Show it to me! Show it to me, Basket! I won't be kept waiting! I demand to see it!

Father Mole-Cricket (*crossing to the hatch*) With your Majesty's permission.

He opens the door of the hatch and the four Pirates enter, each bearing a chest which they lay at the feet of the Emperor

Firstly, Majesty, the missing chests of gold.

Emperor Yes, yes, yes! Never mind about all that, man! Where's the present?

Father Mole-Cricket But, Majesty, this is the present. The ship. A new Royal Yacht.

Emperor A Royal Yacht! For me! It isn't, Gasket!

Father Mole-Cricket It is indeed, Majesty. Isn't it, my boy?

Master Mole-Cricket Indeed it is, Father.

Father Mole-Cricket And a crew to sail her, Majesty. This is the Captain.

Captain (*lumbering forward and extending a grimy hand*) Cluster my cabin, shipmate! Welcome aboard!

Emperor (*shaking hands with the Captain and turning to Father Mole-Cricket*) Docket, I . . . I just don't know what to say. It's . . . it's just what I wanted. Isn't it just what I wanted, Chancellor?

The Chancellor bows low

You must be rewarded for this, Docket. You must both be rewarded. Mustn't they be rewarded, Chancellor?

The Chancellor bows low again

Now let me think . . .

The Chancellor leans forward and whisper in the Emperors ear. The Emperor nods his head

Of course! Of course! Come here, my girl.

The Princess shakes her head

Do as you're told!

The Princess approaches her father reluctantly

And you, young man.

Master Mole-Cricket hesitates

I said, come here! I will be obeyed! I'm the Emperor, aren't I? Where's the fun in being an Emperor if all your subjects please themselves. Come here at once, lad, or I'll lose my temper.

Master Mole-Cricket crosses reluctantly to stand beside the Emperor. The Emperor takes the hand of his daughter and the hand of Master Mole-Cricket and presses them together

If there's one thing I insist upon it's a happy ending. Here, take the girl— and you take him. For goodness sake get married! Though goodness only knows what the pair of you will make of that. Well, smile, bless you! You're both supposed to live happily ever after. Aren't they supposed to live happily ever after, Chancellor?

Chancellor They are indeed, Majesty. It's the usual custom.

Emperor You hear that both of you? It's the usual custom.

Chancellor What is known in general circles, Majesty, as a common practice.

Emperor There! You heard what he said. It's a common—will you be quiet, Chancellor. Let them sort it out for themselves.

Master Mole-Cricket and the Princess, though holding hands, still steadfastly refuse to look at each other. They address their remarks to the audience

Princess I could never marry him. Never in a million years.

Master Mole-Cricket The very idea of a marriage to this girl makes my blood run cold.

Princess I should terrorize him with my temper.

Master Mole-Cricket She would grow to loathe my laziness.

Princess He'd soon grow tired of my tantrums.

Master Mole-Cricket She'd have tantrums whenever I was tired.

Princess I'm quite unsuitable for matrimony.

Master Mole-Cricket If ever there was a boy not meant for marriage—I'm him.

Princess If he were to devote his life to making me happy I wouldn't appreciate it.

Master Mole-Cricket Should she spend all her days indulging all my whims it would be a complete waste of time.

Princess No couple was ever more unsuited.

Master Mole-Cricket You couldn't imagine a worse match.

Princess (*relenting*) I would be the first to admit that the fault is not entirely on his side.

Master Mole-Cricket (*also relenting*) The truth of the matter is that I am just not good enough for her.

They turn to face each other

Princess If I had an ounce of common sense I would run away this very minute.

Master Mole-Cricket If I had an iota of intelligence I'd kill myself.

Princess The trouble is—I haven't a bit of common sense.

Master Mole-Cricket And I have no intelligence.

Princess We can only make the best of it.

Master Mole-Cricket That's the most we can hope for.

They embrace

Emperor You see? I always knew they were meant for each other. And now, Rocket, all that remains to be settled is your own reward. Let me see ... I have it! Casket, I shall appoint you my new Royal Permanent Astrologer! How's that?

Father Mole-Cricket No, thank you very much, Majesty.

Emperor What did you say?

Father Mole-Cricket I said "No, thank you very much, Majesty"! You see, I have had rather a busy day. I do feel tired. I had thought that I might go home and ...

Mother Mole-Cricket And chop the wood and sweep the chimney and clean the yard and scrub the floor and mend the roof on the chicken run and water the crops and plant the rice and ... (*She pauses for breath*)

Father Mole-Cricket When can I take up my duties, Majesty?

Emperor Good, good! Excellent, excellent! I always knew you were a sensible sort of chap, Choppitt. You can begin immediately. I know! I have it! I shall review the Royal Fleet in my new Royal Yacht and you shall come with me! How's that?

Father Mole-Cricket It's very kind of your Majesty.

Emperor Nonsense, nonsense! Of course, there are one or two odds and ends to be carried aboard first. I left them on my flag-ship. My desk, my throne, my furniture—just a few things. Be a good fellow, Brisket, bring them across for me.

Father Mole-Cricket But, Majesty, I have had rather a busy day and it did seem as if I might . . .

Emperor Locket, Locket! You know the punishment for refusing to obey a Royal Command, don't you?

Father Mole-Cricket I didn't even know that there was a punishment, Majesty.

Emperor I'm afraid there is, Cratchitt.

Father Mole-Cricket In which case, Majesty, I rather fear that I can guess what it is.

Emperor I rather thought that you would.

Father Mole-Cricket With your Majesty's permission I will bring the things on board at once.

Emperor Good man.

Father Mole-Cricket exits wearily along the gang-plank

The rest of you are all invited. (*He turns to where the Chancellor stands*) As for you, Chancellor . . . You too, have earned a reward.

The Chancellor bows low

Let me see . . . Ah! I have it! While we're waiting for Picket we'll sail once round the harbour, and you shall have the honour of standing beside me on the bridge!

Chancellor Majesty!

Emperor And, Chancellor, you may ring the ship's bell!

Chancellor Your Majesty is too generous!

Emperor Eh? What's that? Well . . . perhaps you're right. I shall ring the bell. Captain? Are you ready to sail?

Captain Venturing voyages, Majesty! Let's put to sea!

The Emperor and the Captain move off, arm in arm, to the bridge. The two Sailors position themselves on either side of the gang-plank. The Mate follows the Captain to the bridge. Mother Mole-Cricket sits on the ship's locker. Master Mole-Cricket and the Princess cross to stand by the deck-rail. The Chancellor crosses downstage to address the audience

Chancellor And there you are. The argument is ended. The evening draws on and now—it's time for us to leave.

The Lights begin to dim

There'll be a moon tonight. (*He glances upwards*) Stars too, I shouldn't wonder. Not a single cloud as far as the eye can see. Such a beautiful evening for a sail. (*He licks a finger and holds it up*) The wind has dropped—just right—and in the right direction. The sea before us—a sheet of glass. The canvas throbbing at the faintest trace of breeze. What a pleasant way to pass the night. How sad you can't come with us. A pity, too, you didn't see the play. Some other time, perhaps . . . Who knows— perhaps some other time . . .

Emperor (*calling from the bridge*) Chancellor! . . . Chancellor! We're waiting to cast off!

Chancellor Coming, Majesty! I'm coming!

Father Mole-Cricket staggers up the gang-plank with a smaller version of the Royal Throne. He lowers his burden to the deck as the two Sailors lift the gang plank and close the "gate"

Emperor Chancellor, I'm about to lose my temper!

Chancellor Just coming, Majesty (*To the audience*) All happily aboard. Time to depart. I must go. Just one thing more. If there're any critics in the house—Sirs, kindly take note. The part of the Chancellor was played by me. Chancellor, you understand. Two "Ells", one "Ee". Thank you.

Emperor (*ringing the ship's bell*) Chancellor! Chancellor!

Chancellor Here, Majesty. I'm coming now. (*To the audience*) That's all. There's nothing else. Except to say—good-night. (*He bows low*) Good-night. (*He bows low again*)

CURTAIN

FURNITURE AND PROPERTY LIST

ACT I

SCENE 1

On stage: The Mole-Cricket house and veranda
Small tree

Off stage: Cooking pot **(Mother Mole-Cricket)**
Sign board **(Father Mole-Cricket)**

Personal: **Emperor:** scroll

SCENE 2

On stage: As Scene 1

Off stage: Bowl of onions and a knife **(Father Mole-Cricket)**
Telescope **(Master Mole-Cricket)**

Personal: **Chancellor:** large handkerchief, stone in shoe, spectacles, notebook and
pencil
Master Mole-Cricket: spectacles
Palace Messenger: sword, scroll

SCENE 3

On stage: Large ornate throne
Smaller throne
Small oriental table with crystal ball
Yellow duster

Personal: **Chancellor:** scroll, pencil, handkerchief and notebook
Father Mole-Cricket: telescope

ACT II

SCENE 1

On stage: As Act I, Scene 1
Telescope on veranda

Off stage: Bundle of firewood and a small hatchet **(Mother Mole-Cricket)**

Personal: Broom **(Mother Mole-Cricket)**
Leader of the thieves: gold watch and chain
Father Mole-Cricket: pencil and paper
Chancellor: notebook and pencil

SCENE 2

On stage: Tangled ropes and rigging
    Hatchway on the right leading to cabins
    Ship's locker containing 2 bags of powder, 2 wooden ramrods, 2 cotton
     fuses, and with a cannon pointing out to sea on either side
    Untidy heap of sailcloth
    Bridge with companionway to deck
    Long tiller shaft
    Length of rope
    Deck rail

Off stage: Long plank **(Fred** and **Henry)**

Personal: **Captain:** telescope (breakable), large red spotted handkerchief, cutlass
    Fred: brown paper bag containing bread crumbs; pistol and cutlass
    Father Mole-Cricket: telescope
    Henry: pistol and cutlass
    Mate: pistol and cutlass

SCENE 3

On stage: As before but now much tidier
    Harbour backcloth
    Four chests **(Pirates)**

Off stage: Smaller version of the Royal Throne **(Father Mole-Cricket)**

Personal: **Mother Mole-Cricket:** hatchet and firewood

LIGHTING PLOT

Property fittings required: nil

1 interior, 2 exterior settings

ACT I, SCENE 1.

To open: Spotlight on the **Chancellor** in front of the CURTAIN

Cue 1   The CURTAIN rises   (Page 1)
          Full general lighting

ACT I, SCENE 2.   Evening

To open: General effect of evening light

No cues

ACT I, SCENE 3.

To open: Spotlight on the **Chancellor** in front of the CURTAIN

Cue 2   As CURTAIN rises   (Page 21)
          Full general lighting

ACT II, SCENE 1.

To open: Spotlight on the Chancellor in front of the CURTAIN

Cue 3   **Chancellor**: "I shall creep quietly away"   (Page 32)
          Full general lighting

ACT II, SCENE 2.   Day

To open: Full general lighting

          No cues

ACT II, SCENE 3.   Evening

To open: Spotlight on the Chancellor in front of the CURTAIN

Cue 4   **Chancellor** "... the house of Father Mole-Cricket."   (Page 52)
          Full general lighting

Cue 5   **Chancellor** "... it's time for us to leave."   (Page 59)
          Lights begin to dim

EFFECTS PLOT

ACT I

Cue 1   **First voice** (off): "... Indera Maya!"   (Page 25)
           Gong booms loudly

ACT II

No Cues

MADE AND PRINTED IN GREAT BRITAIN BY
LATIMER TREND & COMPANY LTD, PLYMOUTH
MADE IN ENGLAND